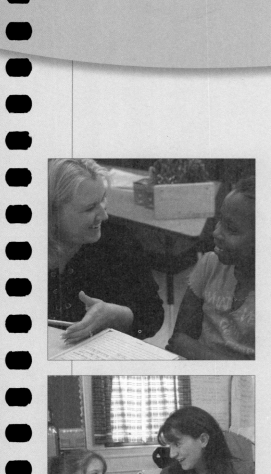

# FOUNTAS & PINNELL

# Benchmark Assessment System **1**

Irene C. Fountas • Gay Su Pinnell

Heinemann
Portsmouth NH

Heinemann
361 Hanover St.
Portsmouth, NH 03801-3912
www.heinemann.com

Offices and agents throughout the world.

Fountas & Pinnell Benchmark Assessment System 1
Assessment Forms

cover: (top) Andrew Swaine, (middle/bottom) Mike Swendner
page vii: (top/middle) Andrew Swaine, (bottom) Mike Swendner
page 201: (top/bottom) Mike Swendner, (middle) Andrew Swaine
page 211: (top/middle) Mike Swendner, (bottom) Andrew Swaine
page 389: (top/middle/bottom) Mike Swendner

ISBN10: 0-325-01185-0
ISBN13: 978-0-325-01185-1

Printed in China
2  3  4  5  6  7  8  NOR  15  14  13  12  11  10  09  08

# Table of Contents

## Recording Forms

## Summary Forms

## Optional Assessments

# Recording Forms

The following section includes the forms you will need to code and score a student's reading of each benchmark book. You will want to photocopy the forms in advance and keep them accessible while you are conducting your benchmark assessment conferences. The Recording Forms are also available on the *Forms CD-ROM*, where they can be printed in regular and enlarged fonts.

Student _____  Grade _____  Date _____

Teacher _____  School _____

## Recording Form
### Part One: Oral Reading

Place the book in front of the student. Read the title and introduction.

*Introduction*:  In this story, two girls tell all the things they like to do together. Read to find out what they like to do. Point under each word as you read.

Sources of Information Used

| Page | Text | | E | SC | E | | | SC | | |
|------|------|---|---|----|---|---|---|----|---|---|
| | | | | | M | S | V | M | S | V |
| 2 | We like to run. | | | | | | | | | |
| 4 | We like to dance. | | | | | | | | | |
| 6 | We like to swing. | | | | | | | | | |
| 8 | We like to climb. | | | | | | | | | |
| 10 | We like to slide. | | | | | | | | | |
| 12 | We like to ride. | | | | | | | | | |
| 14 | We like to paint. | | | | | | | | | |
| 16 | We **love** to read. | | | | | | | | | |
| | **Total** | | | | | | | | | |

*Best Friends* Level A, RW: 32

Recording Forms

| Accuracy Rate | Errors | 4 or more | 3 | 2 | 1 | 0 |
|---|---|---|---|---|---|---|
| | % | Below 90% | 91% | 94% | 97% | 100% |

| Self-Correction Ratio | (E + SC) ÷ SC = 1: _____ |
|---|---|

## Part Two: Comprehension Conversation

Have a conversation with the student, noting the key understandings the student expresses. Use prompts as needed to stimulate discussion of understandings the student does not express. Score for evidence of all understandings expressed—with or without a prompt. Circle the number in the score column that reflects the level of understanding demonstrated.

*Teacher:* Talk about what happened in this story.

**Comprehension Scoring Key**

**0** Reflects **no** understanding of the text. Either does not respond or talks off the topic.

**1** Reflects **very limited** understanding of the text. Mentions a few facts or ideas but does not express the important information or ideas.

**2** Reflects **partial** understanding of the text. Includes important information and ideas but neglects other key understandings.

**3** Reflects **excellent** understanding of the text. Includes almost all important information and main ideas.

| Key Understandings | Prompts | Score |
|---|---|---|
| **Within the Text**<br><br>There are lots of different things the girls like to do together. (Gives 2–3 examples such as run, dance, swing, climb, slide, ride, paint, and read.)<br><br>*Note any additional understandings:* | Tell some things the girls like to do together.<br><br>Can you tell more things they like to do together? | 0  1  2  3 |
| **Beyond the Text**<br><br>The girls like to do things with each other.<br><br>The girls like to read more than they like to do other things.<br><br>*Note any additional understandings:* | How can you tell these girls are best friends?<br><br>Of all the things the girls do together, what's their favorite thing to do? Why? | 0  1  2  3 |

**Guide to Total Score**

**6–7 Excellent** Comprehension

**5   Satisfactory** Comprehension

**4   Limited** Comprehension

**0–3 Unsatisfactory** Comprehension

Subtotal Score: _____ /6

Add 1 for any additional understandings: _____ /1

Total Score: _____ /7

---

## Part Three: Writing About Reading *(optional)*

Read the writing/drawing prompt on the next page to the student. Specify the amount of time for the student to complete the task. (See *Assessment Guide* for more information.)

**Writing About Reading Scoring Key**

**0** Reflects **no** understanding of the text.

**1** Reflects **very limited** understanding of the text.

**2** Reflects **partial** understanding of the text.

**3** Reflects **excellent** understanding of the text.

Student _____     Date _____

# Write about what the two girls like to do together. You can draw a picture to go with your writing.

Student _____  Grade _____  Date _____

Teacher _____  School _____

## Recording Form
### Part One: Oral Reading

Place the book in front of the student. Read the title and introduction.

*Introduction*:  This boy is telling all the things he can do at the park with his dad. Read to find out what he says he can do. Point under each word as you read.

Sources of Information Used

| Page | Text *At the Park* Level A, RW: 24 | E | SC | E | | | SC | | |
|---|---|---|---|---|---|---|---|---|---|
| | | | | M | S | V | M | S | V |
| 2 | I can ride. | | | | | | | | |
| 4 | I can kick. | | | | | | | | |
| 6 | I can catch. | | | | | | | | |
| 8 | I can jump. | | | | | | | | |
| 10 | I can swing. | | | | | | | | |
| 12 | I can slide. | | | | | | | | |
| 14 | I can run. | | | | | | | | |
| 16 | I can hide. | | | | | | | | |
| | **Total** | | | | | | | | |

Recording Forms

| Accuracy Rate | Errors | 3 or more | 2 | 1 | 0 |
|---|---|---|---|---|---|
| | % | Below 90% | 92% | 96% | 100% |

| Self-Correction Ratio | $(E + SC) \div SC = 1:$ ____ |
|---|---|

© 2008 by Irene C. Fountas and Gay Su Pinnell. Portsmouth, NH: Heinemann. This page may be photocopied.

## Part Two: Comprehension Conversation

Have a conversation with the student, noting the key understandings the student expresses. Use prompts as needed to stimulate discussion of understandings the student does not express. Score for evidence of all understandings expressed—with or without a prompt. Circle the number in the score column that reflects the level of understanding demonstrated.

*Teacher:* Talk about what you learned in this book.

**Comprehension Scoring Key**

**0** Reflects **no** understanding of the text. Either does not respond or talks off the topic.

**1** Reflects **very limited** understanding of the text. Mentions a few facts or ideas but does not express the important information or ideas.

**2** Reflects **partial** understanding of the text. Includes important information and ideas but neglects other key understandings.

**3** Reflects **excellent** understanding of the text. Includes almost all important information and main ideas.

| Key Understandings | Prompts | Score |
|---|---|---|
| **Within the Text**<br><br>The boy can do lots of things at the park. (Gives 2–3 examples such as ride, kick, catch, jump, swing, slide, run, and hide.)<br><br>*Note any additional understandings:* | Talk about what things the boy can do at the park. | 0  1  2  3 |
| **Beyond the Text**<br><br>It's fun to (gives opinion or examples from own life) at the park.<br><br>Some other things they could do at the park are (gives examples).<br><br>Some people like to go to the park because they can (be outside and play, have picnics, etc).<br><br>The boy really likes to go to the park with his dad because (gives any reasonable explanation).<br><br>*Note any additional understandings:* | What are some fun things to do at the park?<br><br>Can you think of some other things that the boy and his dad could do at the park?<br><br>Why do people like to go to the park?<br><br>Why do you think the boy likes to go to the park? | 0  1  2  3 |

**Guide to Total Score**

**6–7 Excellent** Comprehension

**5 Satisfactory** Comprehension

**4 Limited** Comprehension

**0–3 Unsatisfactory** Comprehension

Subtotal Score: _____ /6

Add 1 for any additional understandings: _____ /1

Total Score: _____ /7

## Part Three: Writing About Reading *(optional)*

Read the writing/drawing prompt on the next page to the student. Specify the amount of time for the student to complete the task. (See *Assessment Guide* for more information.)

**Writing About Reading Scoring Key**

**0** Reflects **no** understanding of the text.

**1** Reflects **very limited** understanding of the text.

**2** Reflects **partial** understanding of the text.

**3** Reflects **excellent** understanding of the text.

Student _____     Date _____

Write about what the boy can do at the park. You can draw a
picture to go with your writing.

Student _____   Grade _____   Date _____

Teacher _____   School _____

## Recording Form

### Part One: Oral Reading

Place the book in front of the student. Read the title and introduction.

*Introduction*:   This girl has a little dog. Read to find out all the things her little dog likes to do with her. Point under each word as you read.

Sources of Information Used

| Page | Text | E | SC | E M | E S | E V | SC M | SC S | SC V |
|------|------|---|----|----|----|----|----|----|----|
| | *My Little Dog* Level B, RW: 55 | | | | | | | | |
| 2 | My little dog likes to sleep with me. | | | | | | | | |
| 4 | My little dog likes to eat with me. | | | | | | | | |
| 6 | My little dog likes to run with me. | | | | | | | | |
| 8 | He likes to play with me. | | | | | | | | |
| | **Subtotal** | | | | | | | | |

Recording Forms

**Part One: Oral Reading** *continued*

Sources of Information Used

| Page | Text | E | SC | E | | | SC | | |
|------|------|---|----|---|---|---|----|---|---|
| | | | | M | S | V | M | S | V |
| 10 | He likes<br><br>to ride with me. | | | | | | | | |
| 12 | He likes<br><br>to jump with me. | | | | | | | | |
| 14 | My little dog likes<br><br>to read with me. | | | | | | | | |
| 16 | My little dog likes me! | | | | | | | | |
| | **Subtotal** | | | | | | | | |
| | **Total** | | | | | | | | |

Recording Forms

| Accuracy Rate | Errors | 6 or more | 5 | 4 | 3 | 2 | 1 | 0 |
|---|---|---|---|---|---|---|---|---|
| | % | Below 90% | 91% | 93% | 95% | 96% | 98% | 100% |

| Self-Correction Ratio | $(E + SC) \div SC = 1:$ _____ |
|---|---|

© 2008 by Irene C. Fountas and Gay Su Pinnell. Portsmouth, NH: Heinemann. This page may be photocopied.

## Part Two: Comprehension Conversation

Have a conversation with the student, noting the key understandings the student expresses. Use prompts as needed to stimulate discussion of understandings the student does not express. Score for evidence of all understandings expressed—with or without a prompt. Circle the number in the score column that reflects the level of understanding demonstrated.

*Teacher*:   Talk about what happened in this story.

**Comprehension Scoring Key**

**0**   Reflects **no** understanding of the text. Either does not respond or talks off the topic.

**1**   Reflects **very limited** understanding of the text. Mentions a few facts or ideas but does not express the important information or ideas.

**2**   Reflects **partial** understanding of the text. Includes important information and ideas but neglects other key understandings.

**3**   Reflects **excellent** understanding of the text. Includes almost all important information and main ideas.

| Key Understandings | Prompts | Score |
|---|---|---|
| **Within the Text**<br><br>The girl is telling about her little dog and the things he can do.<br><br>The little dog likes to do lots of things with her. (Gives 2–3 examples such as sleep, eat, run, play, ride, jump, and read.)<br><br>*Note any additional understandings:* | What did the girl tell about in the book?<br><br>Tell some of the things this little dog likes to do with the girl. | 0   1   2   3 |
| **Beyond the Text**<br><br>The little dog likes to do lots of things and probably likes to do other things too (gives examples).<br><br>The girl is really proud of (or loves) her dog.<br><br>This dog is like my dog (or makes any personal connection).<br><br>*Note any additional understandings:* | What other things do you think the little dog likes to do with the girl?<br><br>How do you think the girl feels about her little dog?<br><br>Did this book remind you of anything? | 0   1   2   3 |

**Guide to Total Score**

**6–7  Excellent** Comprehension

**5      Satisfactory** Comprehension

**4      Limited** Comprehension

**0–3  Unsatisfactory** Comprehension

Subtotal Score: _____ /6

Add 1 for any additional understandings: _____ /1

Total Score: _____ /7

## Part Three: Writing About Reading *(optional)*

Read the writing/drawing prompt on the next page to the student. Specify the amount of time for the student to complete the task. (See *Assessment Guide* for more information.)

**Writing About Reading Scoring Key**

**0**  Reflects **no** understanding of the text.

**1**  Reflects **very limited** understanding of the text.

**2**  Reflects **partial** understanding of the text.

**3**  Reflects **excellent** understanding of the text.

Student _____ Date _____

Write about three things the little dog likes to do. You can draw a picture to go with your writing.

Recording Forms

Student _____  Grade _____  Date _____

Teacher _____  School _____

## Recording Form

### Part One: Oral Reading

Place the book in front of the student. Read the title and introduction.

*Introduction*:    In this book, a girl is playing with lots of different things. Read about all the things she likes to play with. Point under each word as you read.

Sources of Information Used

| Page | Text                       *Playing* Level B, RW: 56 | E | SC | E M | E S | E V | SC M | SC S | SC V |
|---|---|---|---|---|---|---|---|---|---|
| 2 | I like to play with a truck. | | | | | | | | |
| 4 | I like to play with a car. | | | | | | | | |
| 6 | I like to play with the ball. | | | | | | | | |
| 8 | I like to play with my doll. | | | | | | | | |
| | **Subtotal** | | | | | | | | |

## Part One: Oral Reading *continued*

Sources of Information Used

| Page | Text | E | SC | E | | | SC | | |
|------|------|---|----|---|---|---|----|---|---|
| | | | | M | S | V | M | S | V |
| 10 | I like to play with a train. | | | | | | | | |
| 12 | I like to play with the plane. | | | | | | | | |
| 14 | I like to play with a boat. | | | | | | | | |
| 16 | I like to play with my dog! | | | | | | | | |
| | Subtotal | | | | | | | | |
| | Total | | | | | | | | |

| Accuracy Rate | Errors | 6 or more | 5 | 4 | 3 | 2 | 1 | 0 |
|---|---|---|---|---|---|---|---|---|
| | % | Below 90% | 91% | 93% | 95% | 96% | 98% | 100% |

| Self-Correction Ratio | $(E + SC) \div SC = 1:$ _____ |
|---|---|

## Part Two: Comprehension Conversation

Have a conversation with the student, noting the key understandings the student expresses. Use prompts as needed to stimulate discussion of understandings the student does not express. Score for evidence of all understandings expressed—with or without a prompt. Circle the number in the score column that reflects the level of understanding demonstrated.

*Teacher*: Talk about what you learned in this book.

**Comprehension Scoring Key**

**0** Reflects **no** understanding of the text. Either does not respond or talks off the topic.

**1** Reflects **very limited** understanding of the text. Mentions a few facts or ideas but does not express the important information or ideas.

**2** Reflects **partial** understanding of the text. Includes important information and ideas but neglects other key understandings.

**3** Reflects **excellent** understanding of the text. Includes almost all important information and main ideas.

| Key Understandings | Prompts | Score |
|---|---|---|
| **Within the Text**<br><br>The girl likes to play with lots of different things. (Gives 3–4 examples such as truck, car, ball, doll, train, plane, boat, and dog.)<br><br>*Note any additional understandings:* | Tell some of the things the girl likes to play with.<br><br>What else can you say about what the girl likes to do? | 0   1   2   3 |
| **Beyond the Text**<br><br>Some of the things the girl likes to play with are toys, but a dog is not a toy.<br><br>I like (or have) some of the same things the girl likes to play with.<br><br>The girl is having fun in this book.<br><br>*Note any additional understandings:* | What do you notice about the things the girl likes to play with?<br><br>Does this book make you think of things you like to play with?<br><br>How do you think the girl was feeling in this story? | 0   1   2   3 |

**Guide to Total Score**

**6–7 Excellent** Comprehension

**5 Satisfactory** Comprehension

**4 Limited** Comprehension

**0–3 Unsatisfactory** Comprehension

Subtotal Score: _____ /6

Add 1 for any additional understandings: _____ /1

Total Score: _____ /7

## Part Three: Writing About Reading *(optional)*

Read the writing/drawing prompt on the next page to the student. Specify the amount of time for the student to complete the task. (See *Assessment Guide* for more information.)

**Writing About Reading Scoring Key**

**0** Reflects **no** understanding of the text.

**1** Reflects **very limited** understanding of the text.

**2** Reflects **partial** understanding of the text.

**3** Reflects **excellent** understanding of the text.

Student _____     Date _____

Write about three things the girl likes to play with. You can draw a picture to go with your writing.

© 2008 by Irene C. Fountas and Gay Su Pinnell. Portsmouth, NH: Heinemann. This page may be photocopied.

Student _____    Grade _____    Date _____

Teacher _____    School _____

# Recording Form
## Part One: Oral Reading

Place the book in front of the student. Read the title and introduction.

*Introduction*:    Socks the cat was sleeping in lots of different places, and the girl wanted her to wake up. Read to find out what makes Socks wake up.

Sources of Information Used

| Page | Text     *Socks* Level C, RW: 79 | E | SC | E | | | SC | | |
|---|---|---|---|---|---|---|---|---|---|
| | | | | M | S | V | M | S | V |
| 2 | Socks was sleeping on the bed. "Wake up, Socks!" I said. | | | | | | | | |
| 4 | Socks was sleeping on my chair. I said, "Wake up, Socks!" | | | | | | | | |
| 6 | She was sleeping on the couch. | | | | | | | | |
| | **Subtotal** | | | | | | | | |

Recording Forms

**Part One: Oral Reading** *continued*

Sources of Information Used

| Page | Text | E | SC | E | | | SC | | |
|------|------|---|----|---|---|---|----|---|---|
| | | | | M | S | V | M | S | V |
| **6** *cont.* | "Wake up, Socks!" I said. | | | | | | | | |
| **8** | She was sleeping on the rug. I said, "Wake up, Socks!" | | | | | | | | |
| **10** | She was sleeping by the window. I said, "Socks, wake up!" | | | | | | | | |
| **12** | Socks was sleeping by the door. | | | | | | | | |
| | **Subtotal** | | | | | | | | |

Recording Forms

**Part One: Oral Reading** *continued*

Sources of Information Used

| Page | Text | E | SC | E | | | SC | | |
|---|---|---|---|---|---|---|---|---|---|
| | | | | M | S | V | M | S | V |
| **12** *cont.* | "Wake up!" <br><br> I said. | | | | | | | | |
| **14** | Socks was sleeping <br><br> under the table. <br><br> "I can wake Socks up," <br><br> I said. | | | | | | | | |
| **16** | [Purr] | | | | | | | | |
| | **Subtotal** | | | | | | | | |
| | **Total** | | | | | | | | |

| Accuracy Rate | Errors | 9 or more | 8 | 7 | 6 | 5 | 4 | 3 | 2 | 1 | 0 |
|---|---|---|---|---|---|---|---|---|---|---|---|
| | % | Below 90% | 90% | 91% | 92% | 94% | 95% | 96% | 97% | 99% | 100% |

| Self-Correction Ratio | (E + SC) ÷ SC = 1: _____ |
|---|---|

| Fluency Score | 0 1 2 3 |
|---|---|

**Fluency Scoring Key**

**0** Reads primarily word-by-word with occasional but infrequent or inappropriate phrasing; no smooth or expressive interpretation, irregular pausing, and no attention to author's meaning or punctuation; no stress or inappropriate stress, and slow rate.

**1** Reads primarily in two-word phrases with some three- and four-word groups and some word-by-word reading; almost no smooth, expressive interpretation or pausing guided by author's meaning and punctuation; almost no stress or inappropriate stress, with slow rate most of the time.

**2** Reads primarily in three- or four-word phrase groups; some smooth, expressive interpretation and pausing guided by author's meaning and punctuation; mostly appropriate stress and rate with some slowdowns.

**3** Reads primarily in larger, meaningful phrases or word groups; mostly smooth, expressive interpretation and pausing guided by author's meaning and punctuation; appropriate stress and rate with only a few slowdowns.

## Part Two: Comprehension Conversation

Have a conversation with the student, noting the key understandings the student expresses. Use prompts as needed to stimulate discussion of understandings the student does not express. Score for evidence of all understandings expressed—with or without a prompt. Circle the number in the score column that reflects the level of understanding demonstrated.

*Teacher*:    Talk about what happened in this story.

<table>
<tr><td colspan="2">**Comprehension Scoring Key**</td></tr>
<tr><td>0</td><td>Reflects **no** understanding of the text. Either does not respond or talks off the topic.</td></tr>
<tr><td>1</td><td>Reflects **very limited** understanding of the text. Mentions a few facts or ideas but does not express the important information or ideas.</td></tr>
<tr><td>2</td><td>Reflects **partial** understanding of the text. Includes important information and ideas but neglects other key understandings.</td></tr>
<tr><td>3</td><td>Reflects **excellent** understanding of the text. Includes almost all important information and main ideas.</td></tr>
</table>

| Key Understandings | Prompts | Score |
|---|---|---|
| **Within the Text**<br><br>Socks the cat was sleeping in many different places in the house.<br><br>A girl was trying to wake Socks up but she would not wake up.<br><br>The girl got Socks to wake up with some food.<br><br>*Note any additional understandings:* | Talk about what Socks was doing in this story.<br><br>What happened when the girl told Socks to wake up?<br><br>What happened at the end? | 0   1   2   3 |
| **Beyond the Text**<br><br>Socks was a sleepy (or lazy) cat.<br><br>Socks woke up because she wanted to eat the food.<br><br>*Note any additional understandings:* | Tell what kind of cat you think Socks was.<br><br>Why did Socks wake up? | 0   1   2   3 |

**Guide to Total Score**

**6–7** **Excellent** Comprehension

**5**    **Satisfactory** Comprehension

**4**    **Limited** Comprehension

**0–3** **Unsatisfactory** Comprehension

Subtotal Score: _____ /6

Add 1 for any additional understandings: _____ /1

Total Score: _____ /7

## Part Three: Writing About Reading *(optional)*

Read the writing/drawing prompt on the next page to the student. Specify the amount of time for the student to complete the task. (See *Assessment Guide* for more information.)

**Writing About Reading Scoring Key**

**0** Reflects **no** understanding of the text.

**1** Reflects **very limited** understanding of the text.

**2** Reflects **partial** understanding of the text.

**3** Reflects **excellent** understanding of the text.

Student _____     Date _____

Write about three places that Socks liked to sleep. You can draw
a picture to go with your writing.

Student _____     Grade _____     Date _____

Teacher _____     School _____

## Recording Form
### Part One: Oral Reading

Place the book in front of the student. Read the title and introduction.

*Introduction*:    A boy is helping his mother shop for food in the market. Read
to see what the boy gets for his mom and what she gets for him.

Sources of Information Used

| Page | Text                          *Shopping* Level C, RW: 96 | E | SC | E M | E S | E V | SC M | SC S | SC V |
|------|-----------------------------------------------------------|---|----|-----|-----|-----|------|------|------|
| 2    | "Get some milk," <br><br> said Mom.                       |   |    |     |     |     |      |      |      |
| 3    | I put the milk <br><br> in the cart.                      |   |    |     |     |     |      |      |      |
| 4    | "Get some apples," <br><br> said Mom.                     |   |    |     |     |     |      |      |      |
| 5    | I put the apples <br><br> in the cart.                    |   |    |     |     |     |      |      |      |
|      | **Subtotal**                                              |   |    |     |     |     |      |      |      |

**Part One: Oral Reading** *continued*

Sources of Information Used

| Page | Text | E | SC | E | | | SC | | |
|------|------|---|----|---|---|---|----|---|---|
| | | | | M | S | V | M | S | V |
| 6 | "Get some bananas," Mom said. | | | | | | | | |
| 7 | I put the bananas in the cart. | | | | | | | | |
| 8 | Mom said, "Get some oranges." | | | | | | | | |
| 9 | I put some oranges in the cart. | | | | | | | | |
| 10 | "Get some carrots," Mom said. | | | | | | | | |
| | Subtotal | | | | | | | | |

**Part One: Oral Reading** *continued*

Sources of Information Used

| Page | Text | E | SC | E M | E S | E V | SC M | SC S | SC V |
|------|------|---|----|-----|-----|-----|------|------|------|
| 11 | I put the carrots in the cart. | | | | | | | | |
| 12 | "Get some tomatoes," Mom said. | | | | | | | | |
| 13 | I put the tomatoes in the cart. | | | | | | | | |
| 14 | "Get some bread," said Mom. | | | | | | | | |
| | **Subtotal** | | | | | | | | |

© 2008 by Irene C. Fountas and Gay Su Pinnell. Portsmouth, NH: Heinemann. This page may be photocopied.

**Part One: Oral Reading** *continued*

Sources of Information Used

| Page | Text | E | SC | E M | S | V | SC M | S | V |
|------|------|---|----|----|----|----|----|----|----|
| 15 | I put the bread in the cart. | | | | | | | | |
| 16 | "Get some cookies," I said. Mom put the cookies in the cart. | | | | | | | | |
| | Subtotal | | | | | | | | |
| | Total | | | | | | | | |

Recording Forms

| | Errors | 11 or more | 10 | 9 | 8 | 7 | 6 | 5 | 4 | 3 | 2 | 1 | 0 |
|---|---|---|---|---|---|---|---|---|---|---|---|---|---|
| **Accuracy Rate** | % | Below 90% | 90% | 91% | 92% | 93% | 94% | 95% | 96% | 97% | 98% | 99% | 100% |

**Self-Correction Ratio**

$(E + SC) \div SC = 1:$ _____

**Fluency Score**    0   1   2   3

**Fluency Scoring Key**

**0**   Reads primarily word-by-word with occasional but infrequent or inappropriate phrasing; no smooth or expressive interpretation, irregular pausing, and no attention to author's meaning or punctuation; no stress or inappropriate stress, and slow rate.

**1**   Reads primarily in two-word phrases with some three- and four-word groups and some word-by-word reading; almost no smooth, expressive interpretation or pausing guided by author's meaning and punctuation; almost no stress or inappropriate stress, with slow rate most of the time.

**2**   Reads primarily in three- or four-word phrase groups; some smooth, expressive interpretation and pausing guided by author's meaning and punctuation; mostly appropriate stress and rate with some slowdowns.

**3**   Reads primarily in larger, meaningful phrases or word groups; mostly smooth, expressive interpretation and pausing guided by author's meaning and punctuation; appropriate stress and rate with only a few slowdowns.

## Part Two: Comprehension Conversation

Have a conversation with the student, noting the key understandings the student expresses. Use prompts as needed to stimulate discussion of understandings the student does not express. Score for evidence of all understandings expressed—with or without a prompt. Circle the number in the score column that reflects the level of understanding demonstrated.

*Teacher*:　　Talk about what you learned in this book.

**Comprehension Scoring Key**

**0** Reflects **no** understanding of the text. Either does not respond or talks off the topic.

**1** Reflects **very limited** understanding of the text. Mentions a few facts or ideas but does not express the important information or ideas.

**2** Reflects **partial** understanding of the text. Includes important information and ideas but neglects other key understandings.

**3** Reflects **excellent** understanding of the text. Includes almost all important information and main ideas.

| Key Understandings | Prompts | Score |
|---|---|---|
| **Within the Text**<br><br>The boy got everything his mom told him to get. (Gives 2–3 examples such as milk, apples, bananas, oranges, carrots, tomatoes, and bread.)<br><br>At the end, the mom got the cookies when the boy told her to.<br><br>*Note any additional understandings:* | Tell some of the things the mom told the boy to get.<br><br><br>What happened at the end? | 0　1　2　3 |
| **Beyond the Text**<br><br>The boy liked to help his mom shop.<br><br>The mom got the cookies because the boy had been a good helper.<br><br>The boy thought it was funny (or was happy) that his mom got the cookies.<br><br>*Note any additional understandings:* | Why do you think the boy was getting everything his mom told him to get?<br><br>Why do you think his mom got the cookies?<br><br><br>How do you think the boy felt when his mom got the cookies? | 0　1　2　3 |

**Guide to Total Score**

**6–7 Excellent** Comprehension

**5　Satisfactory** Comprehension

**4　Limited** Comprehension

**0–3 Unsatisfactory** Comprehension

Subtotal Score: _____/6

Add 1 for any additional understandings: _____/1

Total Score: _____/7

## Part Three: Writing About Reading (optional)

Read the writing/drawing prompt on the next page to the student. Specify the amount of time for the student to complete the task. (See *Assessment Guide* for more information.)

**Writing About Reading Scoring Key**

**0** Reflects **no** understanding of the text.

**1** Reflects **very limited** understanding of the text.

**2** Reflects **partial** understanding of the text.

**3** Reflects **excellent** understanding of the text.

Student _____ Date _____

Write about how the boy and his mom helped each other when they were shopping. You can draw a picture to go with your writing.

Student _____  Grade _____  Date _____

Teacher _____  School _____

## Recording Form

### Part One: Oral Reading

Place the book in front of the student. Read the title and introduction.

*Introduction*:  In this story, each animal went into a little house and said, "What a nice little house!"
Read to find out what happened when all the animals went in.

Sources of Information Used

| Page | Text *The Nice Little House* Level D, RW: 129 | E | SC | E | | | SC | | |
|------|------|---|----|---|---|---|----|----|----|
| | | | | M | S | V | M | S | V |
| 2 | The horse went in the little house. "What a nice little house!" said the horse. | | | | | | | | |
| 4 | The cow went in the little house. "What a nice little house!" said the cow. | | | | | | | | |
| 6 | The pig went in the little house. The pig said, | | | | | | | | |
| | **Subtotal** | | | | | | | | |

**Part One: Oral Reading** *continued*

Sources of Information Used

| Page | Text | E | SC | E | | | SC | | |
|------|------|---|----|---|---|---|----|---|---|
| | | | | M | S | V | M | S | V |
| **6** *cont.* | "What a nice<br><br>little house!" | | | | | | | | |
| **8** | The chicken went<br><br>in the little house.<br><br>"What a nice little house!"<br><br>she said. | | | | | | | | |
| **10** | The duck went<br><br>in the little house.<br><br>She said,<br><br>"What a nice<br><br>little house!" | | | | | | | | |
| | **Subtotal** | | | | | | | | |

© 2008 by Irene C. Fountas and Gay Su Pinnell. Portsmouth, NH: Heinemann. This page may be photocopied.

Recording Forms

Recording Forms

## Part One: Oral Reading *continued*

Sources of Information Used

| Page | Text | E | SC | E | | | SC | | |
|------|------|---|----|---|---|---|----|---|---|
| | | | | M | S | V | M | S | V |
| 12 | The  skunk  went<br><br>in  the  little  house.<br><br>Then  .  .  . | | | | | | | | |
| 14 | The  horse  went<br><br>out  of  the  little  house.<br><br>The  cow  went<br><br>out  of  the  little  house. | | | | | | | | |
| 15 | The  pig  went<br><br>out  of  the  little  house.<br><br>The  chicken  went<br><br>out  of  the  little  house. | | | | | | | | |
| | **Subtotal** | | | | | | | | |

## Part One: Oral Reading *continued*

Sources of Information Used

| Page | Text | E | SC | E | | | SC | | |
|------|------|---|----|----|---|---|----|---|---|
| | | | | M | S | V | M | S | V |
| **15** *cont.* | The duck went<br><br>out of the little house. | | | | | | | | |
| **16** | "What a nice **big** house!"<br><br>said the skunk. | | | | | | | | |
| | Subtotal | | | | | | | | |
| | Total | | | | | | | | |

Recording Forms

| | **Errors** | 14 or more | 13 | 11–12 | 10 | 9 | 8 | 6–7 | 5 | 4 | 2–3 | 1 | 0 |
|---|---|---|---|---|---|---|---|---|---|---|---|---|---|
| **Accuracy Rate** | **%** | Below 90% | 90% | 91% | 92% | 93% | 94% | 95% | 96% | 97% | 98% | 99% | 100% |

| **Self-Correction Ratio** | $(E + SC) \div SC = 1:$ \_\_\_\_ |
|---|---|

| **Fluency Score** | 0   1   2   3 |

**Fluency Scoring Key**

**0**   Reads primarily word-by-word with occasional but infrequent or inappropriate phrasing; no smooth or expressive interpretation, irregular pausing, and no attention to author's meaning or punctuation; no stress or inappropriate stress, and slow rate.

**1**   Reads primarily in two-word phrases with some three- and four-word groups and some word-by-word reading; almost no smooth, expressive interpretation or pausing guided by author's meaning and punctuation; almost no stress or inappropriate stress, with slow rate most of the time.

**2**   Reads primarily in three- or four-word phrase groups; some smooth, expressive interpretation and pausing guided by author's meaning and punctuation; mostly appropriate stress and rate with some slowdowns.

**3**   Reads primarily in larger, meaningful phrases or word groups; mostly smooth, expressive interpretation and pausing guided by author's meaning and punctuation; appropriate stress and rate with only a few slowdowns.

## Part Two: Comprehension Conversation

Have a conversation with the student, noting the key understandings the student expresses. Use prompts as needed to stimulate discussion of understandings the student does not express. Score for evidence of all understandings expressed—with or without a prompt. Circle the number in the score column that reflects the level of understanding demonstrated.

*Teacher*:   Talk about what happened in this story.

**Comprehension Scoring Key**

**0**   Reflects **no** understanding of the text. Either does not respond or talks off the topic.

**1**   Reflects **very limited** understanding of the text. Mentions a few facts or ideas but does not express the important information or ideas.

**2**   Reflects **partial** understanding of the text. Includes important information and ideas but neglects other key understandings.

**3**   Reflects **excellent** understanding of the text. Includes almost all important information and main ideas.

| Key Understandings | Prompts | Score |
|---|---|---|
| **Within the Text**<br><br>All the animals went in the little house.<br><br>The skunk went in the house and all the other animals came out (ran away).<br><br>*Note any additional understandings:* | Talk about what happened first in this story.<br><br>Then what happened?<br><br>What happened at the end? | 0   1   2   3 |
| **Beyond the Text**<br><br>The animals did not want to be in the house with the skunk because he might smell it up.<br><br>The skunk felt good when he saw how big the house seemed when he was there by himself.<br><br>The little house was big to the skunk because he was there all by himself (and/or he was little).<br><br>*Note any additional understandings:* | Why did the animals run away?<br><br>How do you think the skunk felt at the end of the story? Why?<br><br>Why did the skunk call it a "nice big house" when all the other animals said it was a "nice little house"? | 0   1   2   3 |

**Guide to Total Score**

**6–7 Excellent** Comprehension

**5**     **Satisfactory** Comprehension

**4**     **Limited** Comprehension

**0–3 Unsatisfactory** Comprehension

Subtotal Score: _____/6

Add 1 for any additional understandings: _____/1

Total Score: _____/7

---

## Part Three: Writing About Reading *(optional)*

Read the writing/drawing prompt on the next page to the student. Specify the amount of time for the student to complete the task. (See *Assessment Guide* for more information.)

**Writing About Reading Scoring Key**

**0** Reflects **no** understanding of the text.

**1** Reflects **very limited** understanding of the text.

**2** Reflects **partial** understanding of the text.

**3** Reflects **excellent** understanding of the text.

Student _____     Date _____

Write about what happened to the animals in the nice little house.
You can draw a picture to go with your writing.

Student _____    Grade _____    Date _____

Teacher _____    School _____

## Recording Form
### Part One: Oral Reading

Place the book in front of the student. Read the title and introduction.

*Introduction*:    Carl has a teacher named Mr. Brown. Carl tells all the things he and the other
children in his class like to do with their teacher, Mr. Brown.

Sources of Information Used

| Page | Text *Our Teacher Mr. Brown* Level D, RW: 113 | E | SC | E M | E S | E V | SC M | SC S | SC V |
|------|-----------------------------------------------|---|----|-----|-----|-----|------|------|------|
| 2 | My name is Carl. I go to school. I like school. This is my teacher. My teacher's name is Mr. Brown. | | | | | | | | |
| 4 | Mr. Brown reads books to us. We like the books. | | | | | | | | |
| 6 | Mr. Brown helps us write stories. | | | | | | | | |
| | **Subtotal** | | | | | | | | |

Recording Forms

Recording Forms

**Part One: Oral Reading** *continued*

Sources of Information Used

| Page | Text | E | SC | E | | | SC | | |
|------|------|---|----|---|---|---|----|---|---|
| | | | | M | S | V | M | S | V |
| **6** *cont.* | We like to write stories.<br><br>We like to read the stories<br><br>to him. | | | | | | | | |
| **8** | Mr. Brown helps us<br><br>read books.<br><br>We like to read books<br><br>to him. | | | | | | | | |
| **10** | We like to paint pictures.<br><br>We like to draw pictures.<br><br>Mr. Brown helps us. | | | | | | | | |
| | **Subtotal** | | | | | | | | |

## Part One: Oral Reading *continued*

Sources of Information Used

| Page | Text | E | SC | E | | | SC | | |
|------|------|---|----|----|----|----|----|----|----|
| | | | | M | S | V | M | S | V |
| 12 | Mr.  Brown  plays  games<br><br>with  us.<br><br>We  like  to  play  ball. | | | | | | | | |
| 14 | We  like  our  school.<br><br>We  like  to  read  books. | | | | | | | | |
| 15 | We  like  to  write  stories.<br><br>We  like  to  play  ball. | | | | | | | | |
| 16 | We  like  our  teacher,  Mr.  Brown! | | | | | | | | |
| | **Subtotal** | | | | | | | | |
| | **Total** | | | | | | | | |

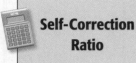

| **Accuracy Rate** | **Errors** | **12 or more** | **11** | **10** | **9** | **8** | **7** | **6** | **4–5** | **3** | **2** | **1** | **0** |
|---|---|---|---|---|---|---|---|---|---|---|---|---|---|
| | **%** | Below 90% | 90% | 91% | 92% | 93% | 94% | 95% | 96% | 97% | 98% | 99% | 100% |

| **Self-Correction Ratio** | (E + SC) ÷ SC = 1: _____ |
|---|---|

| **Fluency Score** | 0  1  2  3 | **Fluency Scoring Key** |
|---|---|---|

**Fluency Scoring Key**

**0** Reads primarily word-by-word with occasional but infrequent or inappropriate phrasing; no smooth or expressive interpretation, irregular pausing, and no attention to author's meaning or punctuation; no stress or inappropriate stress, and slow rate.

**1** Reads primarily in two-word phrases with some three- and four-word groups and some word-by-word reading; almost no smooth, expressive interpretation or pausing guided by author's meaning and punctuation; almost no stress or inappropriate stress, with slow rate most of the time.

**2** Reads primarily in three- or four-word phrase groups; some smooth, expressive interpretation and pausing guided by author's meaning and punctuation; mostly appropriate stress and rate with some slowdowns.

**3** Reads primarily in larger, meaningful phrases or word groups; mostly smooth, expressive interpretation and pausing guided by author's meaning and punctuation; appropriate stress and rate with only a few slowdowns.

## Part Two: Comprehension Conversation

Have a conversation with the student, noting the key understandings the student expresses. Use prompts as needed to stimulate discussion of understandings the student does not express. Score for evidence of all understandings expressed—with or without a prompt. Circle the number in the score column that reflects the level of understanding demonstrated.

*Teacher:*  Talk about what you learned in this book.

**Comprehension Scoring Key**

**0** Reflects **no** understanding of the text. Either does not respond or talks off the topic.

**1** Reflects **very limited** understanding of the text. Mentions a few facts or ideas but does not express the important information or ideas.

**2** Reflects **partial** understanding of the text. Includes important information and ideas but neglects other key understandings.

**3** Reflects **excellent** understanding of the text. Includes almost all important information and main ideas.

| Key Understandings | Prompts | Score |
|---|---|---|
| **Within the Text**<br><br>Carl likes everything he does at school with his teacher. (Gives 2–3 examples, such as read books, write stories, listen to stories, paint pictures, and play ball.)<br><br>Mr. Brown helps Carl and the other children do things at school.<br><br>*Note any additional understandings:* | Carl and the other children like a lot of things they do with their teacher at school, don't they? What were some of those things?<br><br>What does Mr. Brown do in this story? | 0  1  2  3 |
| **Beyond the Text**<br><br>Carl likes school because he likes to (gives 1–2 examples, such as read books, write stories, listen to stories, paint pictures, play ball).<br><br>I think Carl's favorite thing at school is (gives an example) because (any plausible reason).<br><br>Mr. Brown is a good teacher because (any plausible reason).<br><br>They do some things like we do at school, such as (gives 1–2 examples).<br><br>*Note any additional understandings:* | Why do you think Carl likes school?<br><br>What does Carl like most about school? Why do you think he likes that?<br><br>What do you think about Mr. Brown? Why?<br><br>Did this story remind you of your teacher or class? Why? | 0  1  2  3 |

**Guide to Total Score**

**6–7 Excellent** Comprehension

**5**  **Satisfactory** Comprehension

**4**  **Limited** Comprehension

**0–3 Unsatisfactory** Comprehension

Subtotal Score: _____ /6

Add 1 for any additional understandings: _____ /1

Total Score: _____ /7

## Part Three: Writing About Reading *(optional)*

Read the writing/drawing prompt on the next page to the student. Specify the amount of time for the student to complete the task. (See *Assessment Guide* for more information.)

**Writing About Reading Scoring Key**

**0** Reflects **no** understanding of the text.

**1** Reflects **very limited** understanding of the text.

**2** Reflects **partial** understanding of the text.

**3** Reflects **excellent** understanding of the text.

Student _____     Date _____

# Write about three things Mr. Brown helps the children do at school. You can draw a picture to go with your writing.

Student _____     Grade _____     Date _____

Teacher _____     School _____

## Recording Form

### Part One: Oral Reading

**Place the book in front of the student. Read the title and introduction.**

*Introduction*:   Kate had a loose tooth and she tried lots of things to make it come out.
Read to find out what happened to Kate's loose tooth.

Sources of Information Used

| Page | Text | E | SC | E | | | SC | | |
| --- | --- | --- | --- | --- | --- | --- | --- | --- | --- |
| | *The Loose Tooth* Level E, RW: 198 | | | M | S | V | M | S | V |
| 2 | Kate had a loose tooth. <br><br> Her tooth was **very** loose. <br><br> Kate played with her tooth. <br><br> But it did not come out. | | | | | | | | |
| 4 | "Don't play <br><br> with your tooth," <br><br> said Kate's mom. <br><br> "Eat your breakfast." <br><br> "I want my tooth <br><br> to come out," <br><br> said Kate. | | | | | | | | |
| | **Subtotal** | | | | | | | | |

Recording Forms

**Part One: Oral Reading** *continued*

Sources of Information Used

| Page | Text | E | SC | E | | | SC | | |
|------|------|---|----|----|----|----|----|----|----|
| | | | | M | S | V | M | S | V |
| 5 | "Your tooth will fall out," said Mom. Kate wiggled her tooth. But it did not fall out. | | | | | | | | |
| 6 | Kate brushed her teeth after breakfast. She wanted her tooth to come out. She wanted it to come out **now**. | | | | | | | | |
| 7 | She brushed and brushed. She brushed her loose tooth. But it did not fall out. | | | | | | | | |
| | Subtotal | | | | | | | | |

Recording Forms

Recording Forms

## Part One: Oral Reading *continued*

Sources of Information Used

| Page | Text | E | SC | E | | | SC | | |
|------|------|---|----|---|---|---|----|----|----|
| | | | | M | S | V | M | S | V |
| 8 | Kate went to school.<br><br>She played<br><br>with her tooth<br><br>at school. | | | | | | | | |
| 9 | "Don't play with your tooth,"<br><br>said Kate's teacher. | | | | | | | | |
| 10 | Kate played<br><br>with her tooth<br><br>at lunch.<br><br>She wiggled it<br><br>and wiggled it. | | | | | | | | |
| | **Subtotal** | | | | | | | | |

© 2008 by Irene C. Fountas and Gay Su Pinnell. Portsmouth, NH: Heinemann. This page may be photocopied.

**Part One: Oral Reading** *continued*

Sources of Information Used

| Page | Text | E | SC | E | | | SC | | |
|------|------|---|----|---|---|---|----|---|---|
| | | | | M | S | V | M | S | V |
| 11 | "Don't wiggle your tooth," said Ben. "I want to eat my lunch." | | | | | | | | |
| 12 | Kate went home. Her brother played with his blocks. Kate played with her tooth. | | | | | | | | |
| 13 | "It is time to eat," said Mom. "Come and have some soup." | | | | | | | | |
| | **Subtotal** | | | | | | | | |

**Part One: Oral Reading** *continued*

Sources of Information Used

| Page | Text | E | SC | E | | | SC | | |
|------|------|---|----|----|---|---|----|---|---|
| | | | | M | S | V | M | S | V |
| 14 | Kate had some soup. <br><br> She said, <br><br> "Now I want an apple. <br><br> I want a big, big apple." | | | | | | | | |
| 15 | Kate took a big, big <br><br> bite of her apple. | | | | | | | | |
| 16 | "Look, Mom!" Kate said. <br><br> "Look at my tooth **now**!" | | | | | | | | |
| | Subtotal | | | | | | | | |
| | Total | | | | | | | | |

Recording Forms

| Accuracy Rate | Errors | 21 or more | 19–20 | 17–18 | 15–16 | 13–14 | 11–12 | 9–10 | 7–8 | 5–6 | 3–4 | 1–2 | 0 |
|---|---|---|---|---|---|---|---|---|---|---|---|---|---|
| | % | Below 90% | 90% | 91% | 92% | 93% | 94% | 95% | 96% | 97% | 98% | 99% | 100% |

| Self-Correction Ratio | (E + SC) ÷ SC = 1: _____ |
|---|---|

**Fluency Score**    0   1   2   3

**Fluency Scoring Key**

**0**   Reads primarily word-by-word with occasional but infrequent or inappropriate phrasing; no smooth or expressive interpretation, irregular pausing, and no attention to author's meaning or punctuation; no stress or inappropriate stress, and slow rate.

**1**   Reads primarily in two-word phrases with some three- and four-word groups and some word-by-word reading; almost no smooth, expressive interpretation or pausing guided by author's meaning and punctuation; almost no stress or inappropriate stress, with slow rate most of the time.

**2**   Reads primarily in three- or four-word phrase groups; some smooth, expressive interpretation and pausing guided by author's meaning and punctuation; mostly appropriate stress and rate with some slowdowns.

**3**   Reads primarily in larger, meaningful phrases or word groups; mostly smooth, expressive interpretation and pausing guided by author's meaning and punctuation; appropriate stress and rate with only a few slowdowns.

## Part Two: Comprehension Conversation

Have a conversation with the student, noting the key understandings the student expresses. Use prompts as needed to stimulate discussion of understandings the student does not express. Score for evidence of all understandings expressed—with or without a prompt. Circle the number in the score column that reflects the level of understanding demonstrated.

*Teacher*:  Talk about what happened in this story.

**Comprehension Scoring Key**

**0**  Reflects **no** understanding of the text. Either does not respond or talks off the topic.

**1**  Reflects **very limited** understanding of the text. Mentions a few facts or ideas but does not express the important information or ideas.

**2**  Reflects **partial** understanding of the text. Includes important information and ideas but neglects other key understandings.

**3**  Reflects **excellent** understanding of the text. Includes almost all important information and main ideas.

| Key Understandings | Prompts | Score |
|---|---|---|
| **Within the Text**<br><br>Kate had a loose tooth and she was doing everything she could to make it come out. (Gives 2–3 examples, such as wiggled it, played with it, brushed it.)<br><br>In the end, she ate an apple and the tooth came out in her soup!<br><br>*Note any additional understandings:* | What was Kate's problem in the story? What did Kate try to do to solve the problem? What else did she do?<br><br>Talk about how the story ended. | 0   1   2   3 |
| **Beyond the Text**<br><br>Kate really wanted her tooth to come out because (gives a plausible reason).<br><br>She felt great when her tooth finally came out.<br><br><br>Kate's mom wasn't worried because she knew the tooth would come out.<br><br>*Note any additional understandings:* | Why do you think Kate really wanted her tooth to come out?<br><br>Talk about how Kate felt about her tooth at the beginning of the story and at the end of the story.<br><br>What do you think Kate's mom was thinking? | 0   1   2   3 |

**Guide to Total Score**

**6–7 Excellent** Comprehension

**5**    **Satisfactory** Comprehension

**4**    **Limited** Comprehension

**0–3 Unsatisfactory** Comprehension

Subtotal Score: _____ /6

Add 1 for any additional understandings: _____ /1

Total Score: _____ /7

---

## Part Three: Writing About Reading *(optional)*

Read the writing/drawing prompt on the next page to the student. Specify the amount of time for the student to complete the task. (See *Assessment Guide* for more information.)

**Writing About Reading Scoring Key**

**0** Reflects **no** understanding of the text.

**1** Reflects **very limited** understanding of the text.

**2** Reflects **partial** understanding of the text.

**3** Reflects **excellent** understanding of the text.

Student _____    Date _____

Write about the three things Kate did to get her tooth to come out.
You can draw a picture to go with your writing.

Student _____    Grade _____    Date _____

Teacher _____    School _____

## Recording Form

### Part One: Oral Reading

Place the book in front of the student. Read the title and introduction.

*Introduction*:    In this book, the writer tells about all the animals you can see at the zoo.
Read to find out about the animals you can see.

Sources of Information Used

| Page | Text      *The Zoo* Level E, RW: 137 | E | SC | E | | | SC | | |
|---|---|---|---|---|---|---|---|---|---|
| | | | | M | S | V | M | S | V |
| 2 | You can see elephants<br><br>at the zoo.<br><br>The baby elephant can walk<br><br>on the day it is born! | | | | | | | | |
| 4 | You can see brown bears<br><br>at the zoo.<br><br>The baby bears stay<br><br>with their mother. | | | | | | | | |
| 6 | You can see polar bears<br><br>at the zoo. | | | | | | | | |
| | **Subtotal** | | | | | | | | |

**Part One: Oral Reading** *continued*

Sources of Information Used

| Page | Text | E | SC | E | | | SC | | |
|------|------|---|----|---|---|---|----|---|---|
| | | | | M | S | V | M | S | V |
| **6** *cont.* | Their fur is white. The fur keeps them warm. | | | | | | | | |
| **8** | You can see lions at the zoo. The lions are resting. Lions rest for a long time every day. | | | | | | | | |
| **10** | You can see giraffes at the zoo. Giraffes are tall animals. They can eat leaves from the tops of trees. | | | | | | | | |
| | **Subtotal** | | | | | | | | |

**Part One: Oral Reading** *continued*

| Page | Text | E | SC | E | | | SC | | |
|------|------|---|----|---|---|---|----|---|---|
| | | | | M | S | V | M | S | V |
| 12 | You can see penguins<br><br>at the zoo.<br><br>These birds can not fly.<br><br>But they can swim! | | | | | | | | |
| 14 | You can see chimps<br><br>at the zoo.<br><br>The chimps like to climb trees.<br><br>They hold on to the trees<br><br>with their big hands. | | | | | | | | |
| 16 | You can see all the animals<br><br>at the zoo! | | | | | | | | |
| | **Subtotal** | | | | | | | | |
| | **Total** | | | | | | | | |

Sources of Information Used

Recording Forms

| Accuracy Rate | Errors | 15 or more | 14 | 12–13 | 11 | 9–10 | 8 | 7 | 5–6 | 4 | 3 | 1–2 | 0 |
|---|---|---|---|---|---|---|---|---|---|---|---|---|---|
| | % | Below 90% | 90% | 91% | 92% | 93% | 94% | 95% | 96% | 97% | 98% | 99% | 100% |

| Self-Correction Ratio | (E + SC) ÷ SC = 1:____ |
|---|---|

| Fluency Score | 0   1   2   3 | |
|---|---|---|

**Fluency Scoring Key**

**0**   Reads primarily word-by-word with occasional but infrequent or inappropriate phrasing; no smooth or expressive interpretation, irregular pausing, and no attention to author's meaning or punctuation; no stress or inappropriate stress, and slow rate.

**1**   Reads primarily in two-word phrases with some three- and four-word groups and some word-by-word reading; almost no smooth, expressive interpretation or pausing guided by author's meaning and punctuation; almost no stress or inappropriate stress, with slow rate most of the time.

**2**   Reads primarily in three- or four-word phrase groups; some smooth, expressive interpretation and pausing guided by author's meaning and punctuation; mostly appropriate stress and rate with some slowdowns.

**3**   Reads primarily in larger, meaningful phrases or word groups; mostly smooth, expressive interpretation and pausing guided by author's meaning and punctuation; appropriate stress and rate with only a few slowdowns.

Recording Forms

## Part Two: Comprehension Conversation

Have a conversation with the student, noting the key understandings the student expresses. Use prompts as needed to stimulate discussion of understandings the student does not express. Score for evidence of all understandings expressed—with or without a prompt. Circle the number in the score column that reflects the level of understanding demonstrated.

*Teacher:* Talk about what you learned in this book.

**Comprehension Scoring Key**

**0** Reflects **no** understanding of the text. Either does not respond or talks off the topic.

**1** Reflects **very limited** understanding of the text. Mentions a few facts or ideas but does not express the important information or ideas.

**2** Reflects **partial** understanding of the text. Includes important information and ideas but neglects other key understandings.

**3** Reflects **excellent** understanding of the text. Includes almost all important information and main ideas.

| Key Understandings | Prompts | Score |
|---|---|---|
| **Within the Text**<br><br>You can see lots of animals at the zoo. (Gives 2–3 examples such as chimps, elephants, giraffes, penguins, polar bears, lions, and brown bears.)<br><br>Accept a variety of facts about the book such as: lions resting for a long time; chimps liking to climb trees; baby elephants walking on the day they are born; giraffes eating leaves; penguins swimming; polar bears having thick, white fur; baby bears staying with their mother.<br><br>*Note any additional understandings:* | What are some of the animals you can see at the zoo?<br><br>What did you learn about the animals at the zoo? What else did you learn? | 0  1  2  3 |
| **Beyond the Text**<br><br>The zoo is a fun place to go because you can see animals and learn about them.<br><br>This book helps you know what a zoo is like so you may want to go there (or other plausible reason).<br><br>*Note any additional understandings:* | Why do people like to go to the zoo?<br><br>Why do you think this writer wanted to tell you about animals you can see at the zoo? | 0  1  2  3 |

**Guide to Total Score**

**6–7 Excellent** Comprehension

**5 Satisfactory** Comprehension

**4 Limited** Comprehension

**0–3 Unsatisfactory** Comprehension

Subtotal Score: _____ /6

Add 1 for any additional understandings: _____ /1

Total Score: _____ /7

## Part Three: Writing About Reading *(optional)*

Read the writing/drawing prompt on the next page to the student. Specify the amount of time for the student to complete the task. (See *Assessment Guide* for more information.)

**Writing About Reading Scoring Key**

**0** Reflects **no** understanding of the text.

**1** Reflects **very limited** understanding of the text.

**2** Reflects **partial** understanding of the text.

**3** Reflects **excellent** understanding of the text.

Student _____        Date _____

Write about three things you learned about the animals at the zoo.
You can draw a picture to go with your writing.

Student _____  Grade _____  Date _____

Teacher _____  School _____

## Recording Form
### Part One: Oral Reading

Place the book in front of the student. Read the title and introduction.

*Introduction*:   Anna was getting ready for school. Her mom said she might need to get glasses to see better. But Anna didn't want glasses. Read to find out what happened when she got her new glasses.

Sources of Information Used

| Page | Text — *Anna's New Glasses* Level F, RW: 220 | E | SC | E M | E S | E V | SC M | SC S | SC V |
|---|---|---|---|---|---|---|---|---|---|
| 2 | "I am ready for school," said Anna. She had a new red backpack and new shoes. "We have one more thing to do," said her mom. "You may need to get some glasses." | | | | | | | | |
| 4 | "I **don't** need glasses!" said Anna. "You may need glasses to help you read," said her mom. | | | | | | | | |
| | Subtotal | | | | | | | | |

Recording Forms

**Part One: Oral Reading** *continued*

Sources of Information Used

| Page | Text | E | SC | E | | | SC | | |
|------|------|---|----|---|---|---|----|---|---|
| | | | | M | S | V | M | S | V |
| **4** *cont.* | "Do you want to read at school?" | | | | | | | | |
| **5** | "I want to read," said Anna. "I love books! But I don't want glasses." | | | | | | | | |
| **6** | Anna went to the doctor. "You **do** need glasses," said the doctor. | | | | | | | | |
| **7** | Anna looked at the glasses. | | | | | | | | |
| **8** | "I don't like these glasses," she said. | | | | | | | | |
| | **Subtotal** | | | | | | | | |

**Part One: Oral Reading** *continued*

Sources of Information Used

| Page | Text | E | SC | E | | | SC | | |
|---|---|---|---|---|---|---|---|---|---|
| | | | | M | S | V | M | S | V |
| 9 | "Look at the purple glasses," said Mom. Anna put on the purple glasses. | | | | | | | | |
| 11 | Anna put on some red glasses. "I like red and I like these red glasses," she said. "You look great in those glasses," said Mom. | | | | | | | | |
| 12 | It was the first day of school. | | | | | | | | |
| | **Subtotal** | | | | | | | | |

**Part One: Oral Reading** *continued*

Sources of Information Used

| Page | Text | E | SC | E | | | SC | | |
|------|------|---|----|---|---|---|----|---|---|
| | | | | M | S | V | M | S | V |
| **12** *cont.* | Anna put her<br><br>new red glasses in<br><br>her new red backpack. | | | | | | | | |
| **13** | "Don't forget your glasses,"<br><br>said Mom.<br><br>"I put them in my backpack,"<br><br>said Anna.<br><br>"Put your glasses on at school,"<br><br>said Mom. | | | | | | | | |
| **15** | Anna and her mom walked<br><br>to school. | | | | | | | | |
| | **Subtotal** | | | | | | | | |

**Part One: Oral Reading** *continued*

Sources of Information Used

| Page | Text | E | SC | E | | | SC | | |
|---|---|---|---|---|---|---|---|---|---|
| | | | | M | S | V | M | S | V |
| **15** *cont.* | Anna looked at her new teacher.<br><br>She opened her backpack and<br><br>put on her new glasses. | | | | | | | | |
| **16** | "I am Mrs. Bell," the teacher said.<br><br>"I am your new teacher.<br><br>We have the same glasses!"<br><br>Anna smiled.<br><br>"Yes, these are<br><br>**great** glasses!" | | | | | | | | |
| | **Subtotal** | | | | | | | | |
| | **Total** | | | | | | | | |

| Accuracy Rate | Errors | 24 or more | 21–23 | 19–20 | 17–18 | 15–16 | 13–14 | 10–12 | 8–9 | 6–7 | 4–5 | 1–3 | 0 |
|---|---|---|---|---|---|---|---|---|---|---|---|---|---|
| | % | Below 90% | 90% | 91% | 92% | 93% | 94% | 95% | 96% | 97% | 98% | 99% | 100% |

| Self-Correction Ratio | (E + SC) ÷ SC = 1: _____ |
|---|---|

| Fluency Score | 0  1  2  3 |
|---|---|

**Fluency Scoring Key**

**0** Reads primarily word-by-word with occasional but infrequent or inappropriate phrasing; no smooth or expressive interpretation, irregular pausing, and no attention to author's meaning or punctuation; no stress or inappropriate stress, and slow rate.

**1** Reads primarily in two-word phrases with some three- and four-word groups and some word-by-word reading; almost no smooth, expressive interpretation or pausing guided by author's meaning and punctuation; almost no stress or inappropriate stress, with slow rate most of the time.

**2** Reads primarily in three- or four-word phrase groups; some smooth, expressive interpretation and pausing guided by author's meaning and punctuation; mostly appropriate stress and rate with some slowdowns.

**3** Reads primarily in larger, meaningful phrases or word groups; mostly smooth, expressive interpretation and pausing guided by author's meaning and punctuation; appropriate stress and rate with only a few slowdowns.

Recording Forms

## Part Two: Comprehension Conversation

Have a conversation with the student, noting the key understandings the student expresses. Use prompts as needed to stimulate discussion of understandings the student does not express. Score for evidence of all understandings expressed—with or without a prompt. Circle the number in the score column that reflects the level of understanding demonstrated.

*Teacher*:   Talk about what happened in this story.

**Comprehension Scoring Key**

**0**  Reflects **no** understanding of the text. Either does not respond or talks off the topic.

**1**  Reflects **very limited** understanding of the text. Mentions a few facts or ideas but does not express the important information or ideas.

**2**  Reflects **partial** understanding of the text. Includes important information and ideas but neglects other key understandings.

**3**  Reflects **excellent** understanding of the text. Includes almost all important information and main ideas.

| Key Understandings | Prompts | Score |
|---|---|---|
| **Within the Text**<br><br>Anna had to get glasses to see better but she did not want to wear them.<br><br>Recounts the major events of the story, such as: Anna didn't want to get new glasses; she tried on many different glasses and chose red ones; she got some new glasses but she didn't want to wear them; she put them on when she saw that her teacher's glasses were the same as hers.<br><br>*Note any additional understandings:* | What was Anna's problem in this story?<br><br>What happened in this story?<br><br>Then what happened?<br><br>What happened at the end of the story? | 0   1   2   3 |
| **Beyond the Text**<br><br>Anna felt (any suitable descriptive word) about wearing glasses.<br><br>Anna didn't want to wear glasses to school because (any plausible explanation).<br><br>Anna felt good when she saw her teacher had glasses just like hers.<br><br>Other kids (or I) felt the same way as (or different from) Anna about having glasses.<br><br>*Note any additional understandings:* | Talk about how Anna felt at the beginning of the story.<br><br>How did Anna feel about wearing glasses? Why?<br><br>Talk about how Anna felt at the end of the story. Why?<br><br>Did this story remind you of anything? | 0   1   2   3 |

**Guide to Total Score**

**6–7 Excellent** Comprehension

**5**    **Satisfactory** Comprehension

**4**    **Limited** Comprehension

**0–3 Unsatisfactory** Comprehension

Subtotal Score: _____ /6

Add 1 for any additional understandings: _____ /1

Total Score: _____ /7

## Part Three: Writing About Reading *(optional)*

Read the writing/drawing prompt on the next page to the student. Specify the amount of time for the student to complete the task. (See *Assessment Guide* for more information.)

**Writing About Reading Scoring Key**

**0** Reflects **no** understanding of the text.

**1** Reflects **very limited** understanding of the text.

**2** Reflects **partial** understanding of the text.

**3** Reflects **excellent** understanding of the text.

Student _____     Date _____

Write about how Anna felt about her new glasses. You can draw
a picture to go with your writing.

Student _____   Grade _____   Date _____

Teacher _____   School _____

# Recording Form

## Part One: Oral Reading

Place the book in front of the student. Read the title and introduction.

*Introduction*:   Mother Bird makes a nest with sticks and grass and then she lays her eggs in the nest. Read to find out what she does to take care of her new baby birds.

Sources of Information Used

| Page | Text     *From Nest to Bird* Level F, RW: 165 | E | SC | E M | E S | E V | SC M | SC S | SC V |
|------|------|---|----|---|---|---|---|---|---|
| 2 | This is Mother Bird. <br><br> What does Mother Bird do? | | | | | | | | |
| 3 | Mother Bird gets sticks <br><br> and grass. She makes <br><br> a nest. | | | | | | | | |
| 4 | Why does Mother Bird <br><br> need a nest? | | | | | | | | |
| 5 | Mother Bird needs a nest <br><br> for her eggs! | | | | | | | | |
| | **Subtotal** | | | | | | | | |

Recording Forms

**Part One: Oral Reading** *continued*

Sources of Information Used

| Page | Text | E | SC | E | | | SC | | |
|------|------|---|----|---|---|---|----|---|---|
| | | | | M | S | V | M | S | V |
| **5** *cont.* | She lays eggs<br><br>in the nest.<br><br>The eggs are blue. | | | | | | | | |
| **6** | What does Mother Bird<br><br>do now? | | | | | | | | |
| **7** | Mother Bird sits on the eggs.<br>She keeps the eggs warm. | | | | | | | | |
| **8** | Why does Mother Bird<br><br>keep the eggs warm? | | | | | | | | |
| | Subtotal | | | | | | | | |

© 2008 by Irene C. Fountas and Gay Su Pinnell. Portsmouth, NH: Heinemann. This page may be photocopied.

Recording Forms

**Part One: Oral Reading** *continued*

Sources of Information Used

| Page | Text | E | SC | E | | | SC | | |
|---|---|---|---|---|---|---|---|---|---|
| | | | | M | S | V | M | S | V |
| 9 | Baby birds are in the eggs. The baby birds will come out of the eggs soon! | | | | | | | | |
| 10 | The baby birds are out! What does Mother Bird do now? | | | | | | | | |
| 11 | Mother Bird feeds her baby birds. She feeds bugs to them. | | | | | | | | |
| | Subtotal | | | | | | | | |

© 2008 by Irene C. Fountas and Gay Su Pinnell. Portsmouth, NH: Heinemann. This page may be photocopied.

## Part One: Oral Reading *continued*

Sources of Information Used

| Page | Text | E | SC | E | | | SC | | |
|------|------|---|-----|---|---|---|---|---|---|
| | | | | M | S | V | M | S | V |
| 12 | The baby birds chirp and chirp. They want to eat more bugs. Where is Mother Bird? | | | | | | | | |
| 13 | Mother Bird gets more bugs. The baby birds eat and eat. | | | | | | | | |
| 14 | The baby birds hop up and down. Why do they hop? | | | | | | | | |
| | **Subtotal** | | | | | | | | |

**Part One: Oral Reading** *continued*

Sources of Information Used

| Page | Text | E | SC | E | | | SC | | |
|------|------|---|----|---|---|---|----|---|---|
| | | | | M | S | V | M | S | V |
| 15 | The baby birds hop and hop.<br><br>Soon they will fly! | | | | | | | | |
| 16 | Look at the baby birds!<br><br>The baby birds can fly! | | | | | | | | |
| | Subtotal | | | | | | | | |
| | Total | | | | | | | | |

Recording Forms

| | **Errors** | **18 or more** | **16–17** | **15** | **13–14** | **11–12** | **10** | **8–9** | **6–7** | **5** | **3–4** | **1–2** | **0** |
|---|---|---|---|---|---|---|---|---|---|---|---|---|---|
| **Accuracy Rate** | **%** | Below 90% | 90% | 91% | 92% | 93% | 94% | 95% | 96% | 97% | 98% | 99% | 100% |

**Self-Correction Ratio**

(E + SC) ÷ SC = 1:____

**Fluency Score**    0   1   2   3

**Fluency Scoring Key**

**0**   Reads primarily word-by-word with occasional but infrequent or inappropriate phrasing; no smooth or expressive interpretation, irregular pausing, and no attention to author's meaning or punctuation; no stress or inappropriate stress, and slow rate.

**1**   Reads primarily in two-word phrases with some three- and four-word groups and some word-by-word reading; almost no smooth, expressive interpretation or pausing guided by author's meaning and punctuation; almost no stress or inappropriate stress, with slow rate most of the time.

**2**   Reads primarily in three- or four-word phrase groups; some smooth, expressive interpretation and pausing guided by author's meaning and punctuation; mostly appropriate stress and rate with some slowdowns.

**3**   Reads primarily in larger, meaningful phrases or word groups; mostly smooth, expressive interpretation and pausing guided by author's meaning and punctuation; appropriate stress and rate with only a few slowdowns.

## Part Two: Comprehension Conversation

Have a conversation with the student, noting the key understandings the student expresses. Use prompts as needed to stimulate discussion of understandings the student does not express. Score for evidence of all understandings expressed—with or without a prompt. Circle the number in the score column that reflects the level of understanding demonstrated.

*Teacher:* Talk about what you learned in this book.

**Comprehension Scoring Key**

**0** Reflects **no** understanding of the text. Either does not respond or talks off the topic.

**1** Reflects **very limited** understanding of the text. Mentions a few facts or ideas but does not express the important information or ideas.

**2** Reflects **partial** understanding of the text. Includes important information and ideas but neglects other key understandings.

**3** Reflects **excellent** understanding of the text. Includes almost all important information and main ideas.

| Key Understandings | Prompts | Score |
|---|---|---|
| **Within the Text**<br><br>Recounts most of the events in order such as: Mother Bird makes a nest with sticks and grass; she lays eggs; she sits on the eggs; baby birds hatch; she feeds bugs to the baby birds; baby birds hop; baby birds fly.<br><br>*Note any additional understandings:* | What happened first in the book?<br><br>What happened next?<br><br>What happened at the end? | 0   1   2   3 |
| **Beyond the Text**<br><br>The eggs have to stay warm so that the little birds inside can (stay alive, grow).<br><br>Mother Bird needs to do these things because baby birds are helpless and must be taken care of.<br><br>Baby birds have to peck themselves out of the eggs when they are big enough; they can't fly right after they hatch. They have to learn.<br><br>Hopping makes their legs (or wings) stronger.<br><br>*Note any additional understandings:* | Why does Mother Bird have to sit on the nest?<br><br>Why does Mother Bird have to do things for the baby birds?<br><br>What are some of the things the baby birds have to do for themselves?<br><br>Why do you think the little birds hop so much? | 0   1   2   3 |

**Guide to Total Score**
**6–7 Excellent** Comprehension
**5 Satisfactory** Comprehension
**4 Limited** Comprehension
**0–3 Unsatisfactory** Comprehension

Subtotal Score: _____ /6

Add 1 for any additional understandings: _____ /1

Total Score: _____ /7

## Part Three: Writing About Reading *(optional)*

Read the writing/drawing prompt on the next page to the student. Specify the amount of time for the student to complete the task. (See *Assessment Guide* for more information.)

**Writing About Reading Scoring Key**
**0** Reflects **no** understanding of the text.
**1** Reflects **very limited** understanding of the text.
**2** Reflects **partial** understanding of the text.
**3** Reflects **excellent** understanding of the text.

Student _____     Date _____

Write about how Mother Bird took care of her eggs and her baby birds. You can draw a picture to go with your writing.

Recording Forms

Student _____     Grade _____     Date _____

Teacher _____     School _____

## Recording Form

### Part One: Oral Reading

Place the book in front of the student. Read the title and introduction.

*Introduction*:     Nick went to bed but something was missing, and he could not go to sleep.
Read to find out how his mom helped him find what was missing.

Sources of Information Used

| Page | Text                              | E | SC | E M | E S | E V | SC M | SC S | SC V |
|------|-----------------------------------|---|----|-----|-----|-----|------|------|------|
| | *Bedtime for Nick* Level G, RW: 216 | | | | | | | | |
| 2 | Nick was looking at his book. His mom came in and said, "It's time for bed." "Okay, Mom," said Nick. | | | | | | | | |
| 4 | Nick put on his pajamas. He washed his face and brushed his teeth. He was ready for bed. | | | | | | | | |
| 5 | Nick got into his bed. | | | | | | | | |
| | **Subtotal** | | | | | | | | |

**Part One: Oral Reading** *continued*

Sources of Information Used

| Page | Text | E | SC | E | | | SC | | |
|------|------|---|----|---|---|---|----|---|---|
| | | | | M | S | V | M | S | V |
| 6 | "Will you read me a story?" <br><br> Nick asked his mom. <br><br> Mom read the story to Nick. <br><br> Nick liked the story <br><br> about the magic fish. <br><br> When the story was over, <br><br> Nick's mom turned off the light. | | | | | | | | |
| 7 | "Good night, Nick," his mom said. | | | | | | | | |
| 8 | "Will you turn on the nightlight?" <br><br> asked Nick. <br><br> "Okay, Nick," his mom said. <br><br> She turned it on. | | | | | | | | |
| | **Subtotal** | | | | | | | | |

**Part One: Oral Reading** *continued*

Sources of Information Used

| Page | Text | E | SC | E | | | SC | | |
|------|------|---|----|---|---|---|----|---|---|
| | | | | M | S | V | M | S | V |
| 9 | "Good night, Nick," his mom said. <br><br> "Now it's time to go to sleep." | | | | | | | | |
| 10 | "I can't go to sleep," said Nick. <br><br> "I will give you a good night kiss," <br><br> said Nick's mom. | | | | | | | | |
| 11 | "Good night, Nick," his mom said. <br><br> "Go to sleep now." | | | | | | | | |
| 12 | "I **can't** go to sleep," <br><br> said Nick. <br><br> "Will you open the door?" <br><br> he asked. | | | | | | | | |
| | **Subtotal** | | | | | | | | |

© 2008 by Irene C. Fountas and Gay Su Pinnell. Portsmouth, NH: Heinemann. This page may be photocopied.

Part One: Oral Reading *continued*

Sources of Information Used

| Page | Text | E | SC | E | | | SC | | |
|------|------|---|----|---|---|---|----|---|---|
| | | | | M | S | V | M | S | V |
| **12** *cont.* | Nick's mom opened the door.<br><br>Light came into the room. | | | | | | | | |
| **13** | "Good night, Nick," his mom said. | | | | | | | | |
| **14** | "I **can't** go to sleep," said Nick.<br><br>"Something is missing."<br><br>He looked around the room.<br><br>Something came in the door. | | | | | | | | |
| **15** | "Wags! You're late," said Nick.<br><br>"Now **we** can go to sleep." | | | | | | | | |
| | **Subtotal** | | | | | | | | |

**Part One: Oral Reading** *continued*

Sources of Information Used

| Page | Text | E | SC | E | | | SC | | |
|---|---|---|---|---|---|---|---|---|---|
| | | | | M | S | V | M | S | V |
| 16 | "Good night, Nick," said Mom.<br><br>"Good night, Wags."<br><br>"Good night, Mom,"<br><br>said Nick. | | | | | | | | |
| | Subtotal | | | | | | | | |
| | Total | | | | | | | | |

© 2008 by Irene C. Fountas and Gay Su Pinnell. Portsmouth, NH: Heinemann. This page may be photocopied.

| Accuracy Rate | Errors | 23 or more | 21–22 | 19–20 | 17–18 | 15–16 | 12–14 | 10–11 | 8–9 | 6–7 | 4–5 | 1–3 | 0 |
|---|---|---|---|---|---|---|---|---|---|---|---|---|---|
| | % | Below 90% | 90% | 91% | 92% | 93% | 94% | 95% | 96% | 97% | 98% | 99% | 100% |

| Self-Correction Ratio | (E + SC) ÷ SC = 1: ____ |
|---|---|

| Fluency Score | 0  1  2  3 | **Fluency Scoring Key** |
|---|---|---|

**Fluency Scoring Key**

**0**  Reads primarily word-by-word with occasional but infrequent or inappropriate phrasing; no smooth or expressive interpretation, irregular pausing, and no attention to author's meaning or punctuation; no stress or inappropriate stress, and slow rate.

**1**  Reads primarily in two-word phrases with some three- and four-word groups and some word-by-word reading; almost no smooth, expressive interpretation or pausing guided by author's meaning and punctuation; almost no stress or inappropriate stress, with slow rate most of the time.

**2**  Reads primarily in three- or four-word phrase groups; some smooth, expressive interpretation and pausing guided by author's meaning and punctuation; mostly appropriate stress and rate with some slowdowns.

**3**  Reads primarily in larger, meaningful phrases or word groups; mostly smooth, expressive interpretation and pausing guided by author's meaning and punctuation; appropriate stress and rate with only a few slowdowns.

Recording Forms

## Part Two: Comprehension Conversation

Have a conversation with the student, noting the key understandings the student expresses. Use prompts as needed to stimulate discussion of understandings the student does not express. Score for evidence of all understandings expressed—with or without a prompt. Circle the number in the score column that reflects the level of understanding demonstrated.

*Teacher:*   Talk about what happened in this story.

<table>
<tr><td>Comprehension Scoring Key</td></tr>
<tr><td>0   Reflects no understanding of the text. Either does not respond or talks off the topic.</td></tr>
<tr><td>1   Reflects very limited understanding of the text. Mentions a few facts or ideas but does not express the important information or ideas.</td></tr>
<tr><td>2   Reflects partial understanding of the text. Includes important information and ideas but neglects other key understandings.</td></tr>
<tr><td>3   Reflects excellent understanding of the text. Includes almost all important information and main ideas.</td></tr>
</table>

| Key Understandings | Prompts | Score |
|---|---|---|
| **Within the Text**<br><br>Nick got ready for bed. He went to bed but he couldn't go to sleep.<br><br>He told his mom to do different things to help him. (Gives 2–3 examples, such as read a story; turn on the nightlight; give a kiss; open the door.)<br><br>His dog (Wags) came in and then he went to sleep.<br><br>*Note any additional understandings:* | What happened in this story?<br><br>What did Nick ask his mom to do to help him sleep? What else did she do?<br><br>How did the story end? | 0  1  2  3 |
| **Beyond the Text**<br><br>Nick didn't know why he couldn't sleep. (Or, he really did know.)<br><br>Nick missed Wags and that's why he couldn't go to sleep.<br><br>Wags might have been taking a walk with Dad (or any plausible reason).<br><br>Nick loves Wags and that's why he missed him and couldn't sleep.<br><br>*Note any additional understandings:* | Do you think Nick really knew why he couldn't sleep? What makes you think that?<br><br>What was the real reason that Nick couldn't go to sleep?<br><br>I wonder why Wags was so late going to bed. What do you think?<br><br>How do you think Nick feels about Wags? | 0  1  2  3 |

**Guide to Total Score**

**6–7 Excellent** Comprehension

**5**   **Satisfactory** Comprehension

**4**   **Limited** Comprehension

**0–3 Unsatisfactory** Comprehension

Subtotal Score: _____ /6

Add 1 for any additional understandings: _____ /1

Total Score: _____ /7

## Part Three: Writing About Reading *(optional)*

Read the writing/drawing prompt on the next page to the student. Specify the amount of time for the student to complete the task. (See *Assessment Guide* for more information.)

**Writing About Reading Scoring Key**

**0** Reflects **no** understanding of the text.

**1** Reflects **very limited** understanding of the text.

**2** Reflects **partial** understanding of the text.

**3** Reflects **excellent** understanding of the text.

Recording Forms

Student _____     Date _____

Write about Nick and what helped him go to sleep. You can draw
a picture to go with your writing.

Student _____     Grade _____     Date _____

Teacher _____     School _____

# Recording Form

## Part One: Oral Reading

Place the book in front of the student. Read the title and introduction.

*Introduction*:    Bubbles are filled with air like balloons. Read to find out about all different kinds of bubbles and how they are made.

Sources of Information Used

| Page | Text | *Bubbles* Level G, RW: 152 | E | SC | E M | E S | E V | SC M | SC S | SC V |
|------|------|------|---|----|---|---|---|---|---|---|
| 2 | Look at all the bubbles!<br><br>Some bubbles are big<br><br>and some are little. | | | | | | | | | |
| 3 | All these bubbles are made<br><br>with soap and water.<br><br>They are called soap bubbles. | | | | | | | | | |
| 4 | Soap bubbles are pretty.<br><br>They are very shiny,<br><br>and they have lots of colors,<br><br>just like a rainbow. | | | | | | | | | |
| | | **Subtotal** | | | | | | | | |

Recording Forms

**Part One: Oral Reading** *continued*

Sources of Information Used

| Page | Text | E | SC | E | | | SC | | |
|------|------|---|----|---|---|---|----|---|---|
| | | | | M | S | V | M | S | V |
| 6 | What is inside all the bubbles?<br><br>Bubbles are like little balloons.<br><br>They are filled with air. | | | | | | | | |
| 8 | Little bubbles have<br><br>a little air inside.<br><br>Big ones have<br><br>more air inside. | | | | | | | | |
| 9 | This boy is blowing air<br><br>to make a soap bubble. | | | | | | | | |
| | **Subtotal** | | | | | | | | |

## Part One: Oral Reading *continued*

Sources of Information Used

| Page | Text | E | SC | E | | | SC | | |
|------|------|---|----|---|---|---|----|---|---|
| | | | | M | S | V | M | S | V |
| 10 | This girl is blowing air into a straw. The air is going into the girl's milk to make bubbles. | | | | | | | | |
| 12 | Here is an enormous bubble. This bubble is as long as a van! It has lots of air inside. | | | | | | | | |
| | **Subtotal** | | | | | | | | |

© 2008 by Irene C. Fountas and Gay Su Pinnell. Portsmouth, NH: Heinemann. This page may be photocopied.

Recording Forms

**Part One: Oral Reading** *continued*

Sources of Information Used

| Page | Text | E | SC | E | | | SC | | |
|------|------|---|----|---|---|---|----|---|---|
| | | | | M | S | V | M | S | V |
| 14 | Don't forget about bubble gum!<br><br>This boy is blowing air<br><br>into his gum to make<br><br>a big, big bubble.<br><br>If he blows in too much air . . . | | | | | | | | |
| 16 | . . . the bubble will **pop**! | | | | | | | | |
| | Subtotal | | | | | | | | |
| | Total | | | | | | | | |

| Accuracy Rate | Errors | 16 or more | 15 | 13–14 | 12 | 10–11 | 9 | 7–8 | 6 | 4–5 | 3 | 1–2 | 0 |
|---|---|---|---|---|---|---|---|---|---|---|---|---|---|
| | % | Below 90% | 90% | 91% | 92% | 93% | 94% | 95% | 96% | 97% | 98% | 99% | 100% |

**Self-Correction Ratio**

(E + SC) ÷ SC = 1: ____

**Fluency Score**    0   1   2   3

**Fluency Scoring Key**

**0** Reads primarily word-by-word with occasional but infrequent or inappropriate phrasing; no smooth or expressive interpretation, irregular pausing, and no attention to author's meaning or punctuation; no stress or inappropriate stress, and slow rate.

**1** Reads primarily in two-word phrases with some three- and four-word groups and some word-by-word reading; almost no smooth, expressive interpretation or pausing guided by author's meaning and punctuation; almost no stress or inappropriate stress, with slow rate most of the time.

**2** Reads primarily in three- or four-word phrase groups; some smooth, expressive interpretation and pausing guided by author's meaning and punctuation; mostly appropriate stress and rate with some slowdowns.

**3** Reads primarily in larger, meaningful phrases or word groups; mostly smooth, expressive interpretation and pausing guided by author's meaning and punctuation; appropriate stress and rate with only a few slowdowns.

## Part Two: Comprehension Conversation

Have a conversation with the student, noting the key understandings the student expresses. Use prompts as needed to stimulate discussion of understandings the student does not express. Score for evidence of all understandings expressed—with or without a prompt. Circle the number in the score column that reflects the level of understanding demonstrated.

*Teacher*:    Talk about what you learned in this book.

**Comprehension Scoring Key**

**0**   Reflects **no** understanding of the text. Either does not respond or talks off the topic.

**1**   Reflects **very limited** understanding of the text. Mentions a few facts or ideas but does not express the important information or ideas.

**2**   Reflects **partial** understanding of the text. Includes important information and ideas but neglects other key understandings.

**3**   Reflects **excellent** understanding of the text. Includes almost all important information and main ideas.

| Key Understandings | Prompts | Score |
|---|---|---|
| **Within the Text**<br><br>There are all kinds of bubbles. (Names 2–3 examples, such as soap bubbles, milk bubbles, or bubble gum.)<br><br>Recounts 3–4 facts about bubbles from the book such as: can be made with soap and water; can have colors in them; are filled with air; can be made by blowing air; can be big or little; will pop if you blow in too much air.<br><br>*Note any additional understandings:* | What are some kinds of bubbles?<br><br>What did you learn about bubbles?<br><br>What else did you learn about bubbles and how they are made? | 0   1   2   3 |
| **Beyond the Text**<br><br>Bubbles get bigger when they have more air inside them.<br><br>Bubbles are like balloons because they have air inside them.<br><br>Bubbles can pop if they get too much air inside them.<br><br>*Note any additional understandings:* | How do bubbles get bigger?<br><br>How are bubbles like balloons?<br><br>Why do bubbles pop? | 0   1   2   3 |

**Guide to Total Score**

**6–7 Excellent** Comprehension

**5**    **Satisfactory** Comprehension

**4**    **Limited** Comprehension

**0–3 Unsatisfactory** Comprehension

Subtotal Score: _____ /6

Add 1 for any additional understandings: _____ /1

Total Score: _____ /7

## Part Three: Writing About Reading *(optional)*

Read the writing/drawing prompt on the next page to the student. Specify the amount of time for the student to complete the task. (See *Assessment Guide* for more information.)

**Writing About Reading Scoring Key**

**0**  Reflects **no** understanding of the text.

**1**  Reflects **very limited** understanding of the text.

**2**  Reflects **partial** understanding of the text.

**3**  Reflects **excellent** understanding of the text.

Recording Forms

Recording Forms

Student _____    Date _____

Write about three interesting things you learned about bubbles.
You can draw a picture to go with your writing.

Recording Forms

Student _____      Grade _____     Date _____

Teacher _____      School _____

## Recording Form
### Part One: Oral Reading

Place the book in front of the student. Read the title and introduction.

*Introduction*:  Jim was invited to a sleepover party. He was worried about staying at his friend's house and wanted to take his favorite toy Mugsy with him. Read to find out what happened.

Sources of Information Used

| Page | Text *The Sleepover Party* Level H, RW: 288 | E | SC | E | | | SC | | |
|---|---|---|---|---|---|---|---|---|---|
| | | | | M | S | V | M | S | V |
| 2 | Jim was excited<br><br>because he was going<br><br>to a sleepover party!<br><br>But he was also a little worried.<br><br>He had never stayed all night<br><br>at a friend's house. | | | | | | | | |
| 3 | All of Jim's friends were invited<br><br>to the party, too.<br><br>Jim said,<br><br>"See you at Matt's house!"<br><br>But he was still worried. | | | | | | | | |
| | **Subtotal** | | | | | | | | |

## Part One: Oral Reading *continued*

Sources of Information Used

| Page | Text | E | SC | E | | | SC | | |
|------|------|---|-----|---|---|---|---|---|---|
| | | | | M | S | V | M | S | V |
| 4 | Mom helped Jim pack<br><br>for the party.<br><br>"Here are your pajamas<br><br>and your toothbrush," said Mom. | | | | | | | | |
| 5 | Jim wasn't really listening<br><br>because he was worrying.<br><br>"What if I miss Mom?"<br><br>he thought.<br><br>"What if I can't fall asleep?" | | | | | | | | |
| 6 | Mom held up Jim's favorite toy.<br><br>"Do you want to take Mugsy<br><br>with you?" Mom asked.<br><br>Jim always slept with Mugsy. | | | | | | | | |
| | **Subtotal** | | | | | | | | |

© 2008 by Irene C. Fountas and Gay Su Pinnell. Portsmouth, NH: Heinemann. This page may be photocopied.

Recording Forms

**Part One: Oral Reading** *continued*

Sources of Information Used

| Page | Text | E | SC | E | | | SC | | |
|------|------|---|----|---|---|---|----|---|---|
| | | | | M | S | V | M | S | V |
| 7 | Jim did want to bring Mugsy.<br><br>But he was worried.<br><br>"Mugsy is a baby toy,"<br><br>Jim told his mom.<br><br>"I don't want my friends<br><br>to laugh at me.<br><br>I **can't** bring Mugsy." | | | | | | | | |
| 8 | "That's fine," said Mom.<br><br>"Get your sleeping bag.<br><br>I'll zip up your backpack." | | | | | | | | |
| 9 | "Have fun," Mom said.<br><br>"I will," Jim answered.<br><br>But he was still a<br><br>little worried. | | | | | | | | |
| | **Subtotal** | | | | | | | | |

## Part One: Oral Reading *continued*

Sources of Information Used

| Page | Text | E | SC | E M | E S | E V | SC M | SC S | SC V |
|---|---|---|---|---|---|---|---|---|---|
| 10 | All of Jim's friends were at Matt's house. They played games and they ate yummy snacks. Jim was having fun. | | | | | | | | |
| 11 | Then it was time for bed. All the boys went up to Matt's room. | | | | | | | | |
| 12 | Dan opened his backpack and pulled out a toy. "Here is Teddy!" said Dan. "I always sleep with him." Luis opened his backpack. "I have Snapper!" he said. | | | | | | | | |
| | Subtotal | | | | | | | | |

Recording Forms

**Part One: Oral Reading** *continued*

| Page | Text | E | SC | E | | | SC | | |
|------|------|---|----|---|---|---|----|----|----|
| | | | | M | S | V | M | S | V |
| 13 | Josh had a toy, too.<br><br>"I always take Spot with me!"<br><br>he said. | | | | | | | | |
| 14 | "I wish I had Mugsy,"<br><br>Jim thought.<br><br>Matt said, "Jim, are you going<br><br>to get ready for bed?" | | | | | | | | |
| | **Subtotal** | | | | | | | | |

**Part One: Oral Reading** *continued*

Sources of Information Used

| Page | Text | E | SC | E | | | SC | | |
|------|------|---|----|---|---|---|----|---|---|
| | | | | M | S | V | M | S | V |
| 15 | "Sure," said Jim.<br><br>He opened his backpack<br><br>to look for his pajamas. | | | | | | | | |
| 16 | "What's this?" said Jim.<br><br>It was Mugsy!<br><br>Mugsy came to the<br><br>sleepover party after all! | | | | | | | | |
| | Subtotal | | | | | | | | |
| | Total | | | | | | | | |

| Accuracy Rate | Errors | 31 or more | 28–30 | 25–27 | 22–24 | 19–21 | 16–18 | 13–15 | 11–12 | 8–10 | 5–7 | 1–4 | 0 |
|---|---|---|---|---|---|---|---|---|---|---|---|---|---|
| | % | Below 90% | 90% | 91% | 92% | 93% | 94% | 95% | 96% | 97% | 98% | 99% | 100% |

**Self-Correction Ratio**

(E + SC) ÷ SC = 1: _____

**Fluency Score**    0    1    2    3

**Fluency Scoring Key**

**0** Reads primarily word-by-word with occasional but infrequent or inappropriate phrasing; no smooth or expressive interpretation, irregular pausing, and no attention to author's meaning or punctuation; no stress or inappropriate stress, and slow rate.

**1** Reads primarily in two-word phrases with some three- and four-word groups and some word-by-word reading; almost no smooth, expressive interpretation or pausing guided by author's meaning and punctuation; almost no stress or inappropriate stress, with slow rate most of the time.

**2** Reads primarily in three- or four-word phrase groups; some smooth, expressive interpretation and pausing guided by author's meaning and punctuation; mostly appropriate stress and rate with some slowdowns.

**3** Reads primarily in larger, meaningful phrases or word groups; mostly smooth, expressive interpretation and pausing guided by author's meaning and punctuation; appropriate stress and rate with only a few slowdowns.

## Part Two: Comprehension Conversation

Have a conversation with the student, noting the key understandings the student expresses. Use prompts as needed to stimulate discussion of understandings the student does not express. Score for evidence of all understandings expressed—with or without a prompt. Circle the number in the score column that reflects the level of understanding demonstrated.

*Teacher:*    Talk about what happened in this story.

**Comprehension Scoring Key**

**0**   Reflects **no** understanding of the text. Either does not respond or talks off the topic.

**1**   Reflects **very limited** understanding of the text. Mentions a few facts or ideas but does not express the important information or ideas.

**2**   Reflects **partial** understanding of the text. Includes important information and ideas but neglects other key understandings.

**3**   Reflects **excellent** understanding of the text. Includes almost all important information and main ideas.

| Key Understandings | Prompts | Score |
|---|---|---|
| **Within the Text**<br><br>Jim was going to his first sleepover party and he didn't know whether to take his toy.<br><br>Recounts most of the important events of the story in order, such as Jim went to a sleepover party; he didn't know whether to take Mugsy; all the other boys brought their toys; Jim missed Mugsy; Jim found Mugsy in his bag.<br><br>*Note any additional understandings:* | What was the problem in the story?<br><br>What happened in the story?<br><br>Then what happened?<br><br>What was the surprise at the end? | 0   1   2   3 |
| **Beyond the Text**<br><br>Jim was worried about being away from home for the first time.<br><br>Jim was worried that the other kids would make fun of him for bringing Mugsy.<br><br>Mom put Mugsy in Jim's bag.<br><br>Jim was glad to see Mugsy.<br><br>*Note any additional understandings:* | Talk about how Jim felt about going to the sleepover party.<br><br>Why was Jim worried about taking Mugsy to the party?<br><br>How did Mugsy get in Jim's bag? Why do you think his mom did that?<br><br>How did Jim feel at the end of the story? | 0   1   2   3 |

**Guide to Total Score**

**6–7 Excellent** Comprehension

**5**   **Satisfactory** Comprehension

**4**   **Limited** Comprehension

**0–3 Unsatisfactory** Comprehension

Subtotal Score: _____ /6

Add 1 for any additional understandings: _____ /1

Total Score: _____ /7

## Part Three: Writing About Reading *(optional)*

Read the writing/drawing prompt on the next page to the student. Specify the amount of time for the student to complete the task. (See *Assessment Guide* for more information.)

**Writing About Reading Scoring Key**

**0** Reflects **no** understanding of the text.

**1** Reflects **very limited** understanding of the text.

**2** Reflects **partial** understanding of the text.

**3** Reflects **excellent** understanding of the text.

Student _____     Date _____

Write about how Jim felt about the sleepover party at the beginning of the story and how he felt at the end. You can draw a picture to go with your writing.

Student _____  Grade _____  Date _____

Teacher _____  School _____

## Recording Form

### Part One: Oral Reading

Place the book in front of the student. Read the title and introduction.

*Introduction*:  There are many kinds of trucks and they do important jobs. Read to find out about the different kinds of trucks and the jobs they do.

| | | | | Sources of Information Used | | | | | | |
|---|---|---|---|---|---|---|---|---|---|---|
| | | | | **E** | | | **SC** | | | |
| **Page** | **Text** *Trucks* Level H, RW: 188 | **E** | **SC** | **M** | **S** | **V** | **M** | **S** | **V** | |
| 2 | Big trucks are on the road. They are going to many different places. They are going to do many important jobs. | | | | | | | | | |
| 4 | This is a fire truck. Fire trucks help put out fires. This truck has a long hose that shoots water on the fire. | | | | | | | | | |
| | **Subtotal** | | | | | | | | | |

© 2008 by Irene C. Fountas and Gay Su Pinnell. Portsmouth, NH: Heinemann. This page may be photocopied.

## Part One: Oral Reading *continued*

Sources of Information Used

| Page | Text | E | SC | E | | | SC | | |
|------|------|---|----|---|---|---|----|---|---|
| | | | | M | S | V | M | S | V |
| 6 | This truck picks up trash.<br><br>The trash goes in the back<br><br>of the truck.<br><br>The truck crushes the trash<br><br>to make it smaller.<br><br>Then the truck<br><br>carries the trash away. | | | | | | | | |
| 8 | This is a mail truck.<br><br>It picks up mail<br><br>from the post office.<br><br>Then the truck carries the mail<br><br>all over town. | | | | | | | | |
| | **Subtotal** | | | | | | | | |

**Part One: Oral Reading** *continued*

| Page | Text | E | SC | E | | | SC | | |
|---|---|---|---|---|---|---|---|---|---|
| | | | | M | S | V | M | S | V |
| 10 | This big truck is a snowplow. It pushes the snow to the side of the road. Then big trucks come to carry the piles of snow away. | | | | | | | | |
| 12 | This truck carries all kinds of food. The truck picks up corn at the farm. Then it takes the corn to the market. | | | | | | | | |
| | **Subtotal** | | | | | | | | |

Sources of Information Used

© 2008 by Irene C. Fountas and Gay Su Pinnell. Portsmouth, NH: Heinemann. This page may be photocopied.

**Part One: Oral Reading** *continued*

Sources of Information Used

| Page | Text | E | SC | E | | | SC | | |
|------|------|---|----|---|---|---|----|---|---|
| | | | | M | S | V | M | S | V |
| 14 | This is an ice cream truck. The ice cream truck plays a song. Children hear the song and run to get ice cream. | | | | | | | | |
| 16 | All kinds of trucks are on the road. Some trucks are for work. And some trucks are for play. | | | | | | | | |
| | Subtotal | | | | | | | | |
| | Total | | | | | | | | |

| | **Errors** | **20 or more** | **18–19** | **16–17** | **15** | **13–14** | **11–12** | **9–10** | **7–8** | **5–6** | **3–4** | **1–2** | **0** |
|---|---|---|---|---|---|---|---|---|---|---|---|---|---|
| **Accuracy Rate** | **%** | Below 90% | 90% | 91% | 92% | 93% | 94% | 95% | 96% | 97% | 98% | 99% | 100% |

| | |
|---|---|
| **Self-Correction Ratio** | $(E + SC) \div SC = 1:$ ____ |

| | | |
|---|---|---|
| **Fluency Score** | 0   1   2   3 | **Fluency Scoring Key** |

**Fluency Scoring Key**

**0**  Reads primarily word-by-word with occasional but infrequent or inappropriate phrasing; no smooth or expressive interpretation, irregular pausing, and no attention to author's meaning or punctuation; no stress or inappropriate stress, and slow rate.

**1**  Reads primarily in two-word phrases with some three- and four-word groups and some word-by-word reading; almost no smooth, expressive interpretation or pausing guided by author's meaning and punctuation; almost no stress or inappropriate stress, with slow rate most of the time.

**2**  Reads primarily in three- or four-word phrase groups; some smooth, expressive interpretation and pausing guided by author's meaning and punctuation; mostly appropriate stress and rate with some slowdowns.

**3**  Reads primarily in larger, meaningful phrases or word groups; mostly smooth, expressive interpretation and pausing guided by author's meaning and punctuation; appropriate stress and rate with only a few slowdowns.

## Part Two: Comprehension Conversation

Have a conversation with the student, noting the key understandings the student expresses. Use prompts as needed to stimulate discussion of understandings the student does not express. Score for evidence of all understandings expressed—with or without a prompt. Circle the number in the score column that reflects the level of understanding demonstrated.

*Teacher:* Talk about what you learned in this book.

**Comprehension Scoring Key**

**0** Reflects **no** understanding of the text. Either does not respond or talks off the topic.

**1** Reflects **very limited** understanding of the text. Mentions a few facts or ideas but does not express the important information or ideas.

**2** Reflects **partial** understanding of the text. Includes important information and ideas but neglects other key understandings.

**3** Reflects **excellent** understanding of the text. Includes almost all important information and main ideas.

| Key Understandings | Prompts | Score |
|---|---|---|
| **Within the Text**<br><br>There are different kinds of trucks and they do different things. (Names 2–3 trucks such as fire truck, trash truck, mail truck, snowplow, food truck, ice cream truck.)<br><br>Trucks do many different jobs. (Gives 1–3 examples such as: a fire truck has a long hose and puts out fires; a trash truck crushes trash; a mail truck picks up and carries mail; a snowplow carries snow away; some trucks carry food; an ice cream truck sells ice cream and plays a song; a toy truck is for play.)<br><br>*Note any additional understandings:* | Tell what you learned about trucks from reading this book.<br><br>Tell me more about different kinds of trucks and the jobs they do. | 0  1  2  3 |
| **Beyond the Text**<br><br>People need trucks because (gives a plausible reason).<br><br>The toy truck is different from all the other trucks because (gives 2–3 reasons such as it is little; it is used for play; it doesn't do jobs for people).<br><br>*Note any additional understandings:* | Why are trucks important to us?<br><br>How is the truck on the last page different from all the other trucks? | 0  1  2  3 |

**Guide to Total Score**

**6–7 Excellent** Comprehension

**5 Satisfactory** Comprehension

**4 Limited** Comprehension

**0–3 Unsatisfactory** Comprehension

Subtotal Score: _____ /6

Add 1 for any additional understandings: _____ /1

Total Score: _____ /7

## Part Three: Writing About Reading *(optional)*

Read the writing/drawing prompt on the next page to the student. Specify the amount of time for the student to complete the task. (See *Assessment Guide* for more information.)

**Writing About Reading Scoring Key**

**0** Reflects **no** understanding of the text.

**1** Reflects **very limited** understanding of the text.

**2** Reflects **partial** understanding of the text.

**3** Reflects **excellent** understanding of the text.

Student _____ Date _____

Write about three things you learned about trucks and the important jobs they do. You can draw a picture to go with your writing.

© 2008 by Irene C. Fountas and Gay Su Pinnell. Portsmouth, NH: Heinemann. This page may be photocopied.

Student _____  Grade _____  Date _____

Teacher _____  School _____

## Recording Form
### Part One: Oral Reading

Place the book in front of the student. Read the title and introduction.

*Introduction*:  A boy named Spencer went to a farm to pick out a cat, but he had trouble finding the best cat. Read to find out if Spencer found the best cat for him.

Sources of Information Used

| Page | Text *The Best Cat* Level I, RW: 263 | E | SC | E | | | SC | | |
|---|---|---|---|---|---|---|---|---|---|
| | | | | M | S | V | M | S | V |
| 2 | Spencer wanted a cat more than anything in the world. He wanted a cat that would sleep on his bed and purr in his ear and be his best furry friend. | | | | | | | | |
| 3 | "Please, can I get a cat?" Spencer asked. "I **really** want one." "Are you sure?" his mother answered. | | | | | | | | |
| | Subtotal | | | | | | | | |

**Part One: Oral Reading** *continued*

Sources of Information Used

| Page | Text | E | SC | E | | | SC | | |
|------|------|---|----|---|---|---|----|---|---|
| | | | | M | S | V | M | S | V |
| **3** *cont.* | "It is hard work<br><br>to take care of a cat." | | | | | | | | |
| **4** | "I'll take good care of him,"<br><br>said Spencer. "I promise.<br><br>I'll brush him and feed him<br><br>and give him water every day."<br><br>"All right," said his mother.<br><br>"Let's go to Apple Tree Farm.<br><br>Maybe we can get a cat there." | | | | | | | | |
| **6** | Spencer and his mother went<br><br>to Apple Tree Farm.<br><br>Many animals lived on the farm.<br><br>There were cows and horses<br><br>in the fields. | | | | | | | | |
| | **Subtotal** | | | | | | | | |

**Part One: Oral Reading** *continued*

Sources of Information Used

| Page | Text | E | SC | E | | | SC | | |
|---|---|---|---|---|---|---|---|---|---|
| | | | | M | S | V | M | S | V |
| **6** cont. | There was a friendly farmer.<br><br>And there were cats everywhere! | | | | | | | | |
| **8** | Spencer had never seen<br><br>so many cats and kittens! | | | | | | | | |
| **9** | "How will you choose just one?"<br><br>asked Spencer's mother.<br><br>Spencer thought about it.<br><br>Then he said, "I'll choose<br><br>the best cat for me." | | | | | | | | |
| | Subtotal | | | | | | | | |

## Part One: Oral Reading *continued*

Sources of Information Used

| Page | Text | E | SC | E | | | SC | | |
|------|------|---|----|---|---|---|----|----|---|
| | | | | M | S | V | M | S | V |
| 10 | Spencer saw a black cat<br>playing on the straw in the barn.<br>"I like your shiny fur,"<br>said Spencer.<br>"Will you be my cat?" | | | | | | | | |
| 11 | The cat ducked under the straw.<br>"I guess you're not the best cat<br>for me," said Spencer.<br>"I'll look for another cat." | | | | | | | | |
| 12 | Spencer watched another cat<br>licking her paw down by the pond.<br>"I like your fluffy tail and | | | | | | | | |
| | **Subtotal** | | | | | | | | |

**Part One: Oral Reading** *continued*

| Page | Text | E | SC | E | | | SC | | |
|------|------|---|----|---|---|---|----|---|---|
| | | | | M | S | V | M | S | V |
| **12** *cont.* | your pink tongue," said Spencer.<br><br>"Will you be my cat?" | | | | | | | | |
| **13** | The cat didn't even<br><br>look at Spencer.<br><br>"I can tell that you are not<br><br>the best cat for me,"<br><br>Spencer said.<br><br>"I'll look for another cat." | | | | | | | | |
| | **Subtotal** | | | | | | | | |
| | **Total** | | | | | | | | |

Sources of Information Used

Have the student finish reading the book silently.

Recording Forms

| Accuracy Rate | **Errors** | **28 or more** | **25–27** | **23–24** | **20–22** | **18–19** | **15–17** | **12–14** | **10–11** | **7–9** | **4–6** | **1–3** | **0** |
|---|---|---|---|---|---|---|---|---|---|---|---|---|---|
| | **%** | Below 90% | 90% | 91% | 92% | 93% | 94% | 95% | 96% | 97% | 98% | 99% | 100% |

| Self-Correction Ratio | $(E + SC) \div SC = 1:\underline{\quad}$ |
|---|---|

| Fluency Score | 0   1   2   3 | |
|---|---|---|

**Fluency Scoring Key**

**0** Reads primarily word-by-word with occasional but infrequent or inappropriate phrasing; no smooth or expressive interpretation, irregular pausing, and no attention to author's meaning or punctuation; no stress or inappropriate stress, and slow rate.

**1** Reads primarily in two-word phrases with some three- and four-word groups and some word-by-word reading; almost no smooth, expressive interpretation or pausing guided by author's meaning and punctuation; almost no stress or inappropriate stress, with slow rate most of the time.

**2** Reads primarily in three- or four-word phrase groups; some smooth, expressive interpretation and pausing guided by author's meaning and punctuation; mostly appropriate stress and rate with some slowdowns.

**3** Reads primarily in larger, meaningful phrases or word groups; mostly smooth, expressive interpretation and pausing guided by author's meaning and punctuation; appropriate stress and rate with only a few slowdowns.

## Part Two: Comprehension Conversation

Have a conversation with the student, noting the key understandings the student expresses. Use prompts as needed to stimulate discussion of understandings the student does not express. Score for evidence of all understandings expressed—with or without a prompt. Circle the number in the score column that reflects the level of understanding demonstrated.

*Teacher*:   Talk about what happened in this story.

<table>
<tr><td colspan="2">**Comprehension Scoring Key**</td></tr>
<tr><td>**0**</td><td>Reflects **no** understanding of the text. Either does not respond or talks off the topic.</td></tr>
<tr><td>**1**</td><td>Reflects **very limited** understanding of the text. Mentions a few facts or ideas but does not express the important information or ideas.</td></tr>
<tr><td>**2**</td><td>Reflects **partial** understanding of the text. Includes important information and ideas but neglects other key understandings.</td></tr>
<tr><td>**3**</td><td>Reflects **excellent** understanding of the text. Includes almost all important information and main ideas.</td></tr>
</table>

| Key Understandings | Prompts | Score |
|---|---|---|
| **Within the Text**<br><br>Spencer went to a farm to get a cat but he could not find one. Finally, he did find a cat.<br><br>Recounts some essential information from the text, such as: the boy went to the farm to choose a cat; something was wrong with all the cats he saw; finally, a little cat chose him.<br><br>*Note any additional understandings:* | What was the problem in the story?<br><br><br>How was Spencer's problem solved? Tell what the boy did to find the best cat for him. | 0   1   2   3 |
| **Beyond the Text**<br><br>Spencer really wanted a cat because (gives a plausible reason).<br><br>Spencer was disappointed (or sad) when none of the cats at the farm were the right cat.<br><br>The little cat wanted a home and the cat really chose the boy.<br><br>Spencer was glad the cat chose him.<br><br>It would be a good way to get a cat because (gives a plausible reason).<br><br>*Note any additional understandings:* | Tell why you think Spencer wanted a cat (or what kind of cat the boy really wanted).<br><br>Tell how Spencer felt when he couldn't find a cat (or how he felt at the end).<br><br>Why do you think the little cat was the best cat for Spencer?<br><br>How did Spencer feel at the end?<br><br>Do you think this was a good way for Spencer to find a cat? Why? | 0   1   2   3 |

**Guide to Total Score**

**6–7 Excellent** Comprehension

**5**   **Satisfactory** Comprehension

**4**   **Limited** Comprehension

**0–3 Unsatisfactory** Comprehension

Subtotal Score: _____ /6

Add 1 for any additional understandings: _____ /1

Total Score: _____ /7

© 2008 by Irene C. Fountas and Gay Su Pinnell, Portsmouth, NH: Heinemann. This page may be photocopied.

## Part Three: Writing About Reading *(optional)*

Read the writing/drawing prompt on the next page to the student. Specify the amount of time for the student to complete the task. (See *Assessment Guide* for more information.)

**Writing About Reading Scoring Key**

**0** Reflects **no** understanding of the text.

**1** Reflects **very limited** understanding of the text.

**2** Reflects **partial** understanding of the text.

**3** Reflects **excellent** understanding of the text.

Student _____    Date _____

Write about Spencer and how he found the best cat. You can draw a picture to go with your writing.

Student _____ Grade _____ Date _____

Teacher _____ School _____

## Recording Form

### Part One: Oral Reading

Place the book in front of the student. Read the title and introduction.

*Introduction*:   Koalas are animals that live in a country called Australia. Read this book to learn all about how koalas live, what they eat, and about their babies.

Sources of Information Used

| Page | Text — *All About Koalas* Level I, RW: 217 | E | SC | E | | | SC | | |
|------|------|---|----|---|---|---|----|---|---|
| | | | | M | S | V | M | S | V |
| 2 | This is a koala.<br><br>It comes from Australia. | | | | | | | | |
| 3 | Koalas live in tall trees<br><br>called gum trees.<br><br>Koalas have sharp claws.<br><br>The claws help them<br><br>climb the trees. | | | | | | | | |
| 4 | Koalas have thick fur<br><br>and white chests. | | | | | | | | |
| | **Subtotal** | | | | | | | | |

**Part One: Oral Reading** *continued*

Sources of Information Used

| Page | Text | E | SC | E | | | SC | | |
|------|------|---|----|---|---|---|----|---|---|
| | | | | M | S | V | M | S | V |
| 5 | They have fluffy ears and big noses! | | | | | | | | |
| 6 | The koala's nose helps it find food. Koalas eat gum leaves. | | | | | | | | |
| 7 | Koalas sleep in the day. At night, they wake up to eat. | | | | | | | | |
| 8 | Koalas do not drink water. There is water in the leaves koalas eat. They get food and water at the same time. | | | | | | | | |
| | **Subtotal** | | | | | | | | |

**Part One: Oral Reading** *continued*

| | | | | Sources of Information Used | | | | | |
|---|---|---|---|---|---|---|---|---|---|
| | | | | **E** | | | **SC** | | |
| **Page** | **Text** | **E** | **SC** | **M** | **S** | **V** | **M** | **S** | **V** |
| 9 | This is a baby koala.<br><br>A young koala is called a joey,<br><br>just like a baby kangaroo.<br><br>When a joey is born,<br><br>it has no hair. | | | | | | | | |
| 10 | A koala joey is very small.<br><br>The little koala stays<br><br>in its mother's special pouch. | | | | | | | | |
| 11 | In the pouch, the baby koala<br><br>drinks its mother's milk. | | | | | | | | |
| | **Subtotal** | | | | | | | | |

**Part One: Oral Reading** *continued*

Sources of Information Used

| Page | Text | E | SC | E M | E S | E V | SC M | SC S | SC V |
|------|------|---|----|----|----|----|----|----|----|
| 12 | This joey is seven months old. It is as long as a loaf of bread. | | | | | | | | |
| 13 | The joey travels on its mother's back. It uses its thumbs to hold on. | | | | | | | | |
| 14 | Koalas "talk" to each other. Mothers and babies make soft sounds. Koalas make deep sounds when they are far away. | | | | | | | | |
| | **Subtotal** | | | | | | | | |

## Part One: Oral Reading *continued*

Sources of Information Used

| Page | Text | E | SC | E | | | SC | | |
|------|------|---|----|---|---|---|----|---|---|
| | | | | M | S | V | M | S | V |
| 15 | Koalas have a problem today.<br><br>Some people are cutting down<br><br>trees to make room<br><br>for houses. | | | | | | | | |
| 16 | Many people want<br><br>to save these trees.<br><br>Koalas need a safe<br><br>place to call home. | | | | | | | | |
| | Subtotal | | | | | | | | |
| | Total | | | | | | | | |

Recording Forms

| Accuracy Rate | Errors | 23 or more | 21–22 | 19–20 | 17–18 | 15–16 | 12–14 | 10–11 | 8–9 | 6–7 | 4–5 | 1–3 | 0 |
|---|---|---|---|---|---|---|---|---|---|---|---|---|---|
| | % | Below 90% | 90% | 91% | 92% | 93% | 94% | 95% | 96% | 97% | 98% | 99% | 100% |

| Self-Correction Ratio | $(E + SC) \div SC = 1:$ \_\_\_\_ |
|---|---|

| Fluency Score | 0   1   2   3 | **Fluency Scoring Key** |
|---|---|---|

**Fluency Scoring Key**

**0**   Reads primarily word-by-word with occasional but infrequent or inappropriate phrasing; no smooth or expressive interpretation, irregular pausing, and no attention to author's meaning or punctuation; no stress or inappropriate stress, and slow rate.

**1**   Reads primarily in two-word phrases with some three- and four-word groups and some word-by-word reading; almost no smooth, expressive interpretation or pausing guided by author's meaning and punctuation; almost no stress or inappropriate stress, with slow rate most of the time.

**2**   Reads primarily in three- or four-word phrase groups; some smooth, expressive interpretation and pausing guided by author's meaning and punctuation; mostly appropriate stress and rate with some slowdowns.

**3**   Reads primarily in larger, meaningful phrases or word groups; mostly smooth, expressive interpretation and pausing guided by author's meaning and punctuation; appropriate stress and rate with only a few slowdowns.

## Part Two: Comprehension Conversation

Have a conversation with the student, noting the key understandings the student expresses. Use prompts as needed to stimulate discussion of understandings the student does not express. Score for evidence of all understandings expressed—with or without a prompt. Circle the number in the score column that reflects the level of understanding demonstrated.

*Teacher:* Talk about what you learned in this book.

<table>
<tr><td colspan="2">**Comprehension Scoring Key**</td></tr>
<tr><td>**0**</td><td>Reflects **no** understanding of the text. Either does not respond or talks off the topic.</td></tr>
<tr><td>**1**</td><td>Reflects **very limited** understanding of the text. Mentions a few facts or ideas but does not express the important information or ideas.</td></tr>
<tr><td>**2**</td><td>Reflects **partial** understanding of the text. Includes important information and ideas but neglects other key understandings.</td></tr>
<tr><td>**3**</td><td>Reflects **excellent** understanding of the text. Includes almost all important information and main ideas.</td></tr>
</table>

| Key Understandings | Prompts | Score |
|---|---|---|
| **Within the Text**<br><br>Names several facts about koalas such as: live in tall gum trees; have sharp claws; have thick fur and white chests; have fluffy ears; eat leaves; sleep in the day; don't drink water; have babies called joeys that don't have any hair.<br><br>*Note any additional understandings:* | Talk about what you learned about koalas. What else did you learn? | 0   1   2   3 |
| **Beyond the Text**<br><br>Koalas are like kangaroos (or any plausible comparison).<br><br>Koalas' bodies help them climb tall trees.<br><br>A baby koala could not live by itself; it has to be in the mother's pouch because it is so young (or little).<br><br>Trees are important to koalas because they are safe there and they eat the leaves.<br><br>Cutting down trees is bad for koalas because they need them to eat and live in.<br><br>*Note any additional understandings:* | Do koalas remind you of any other animals?<br><br>What helps the koalas climb tall trees?<br><br>Why does the joey stay in the mother's pouch?<br><br>Why are trees important to koalas?<br><br>What could happen if all of the trees are cut down? | 0   1   2   3 |

**Guide to Total Score**

**6–7 Excellent** Comprehension

**5 Satisfactory** Comprehension

**4 Limited** Comprehension

**0–3 Unsatisfactory** Comprehension

Subtotal Score: _____/6

Add 1 for any additional understandings: _____/1

Total Score: _____/7

## Part Three: Writing About Reading *(optional)*

Read the writing/drawing prompt on the next page to the student. Specify the amount of time for the student to complete the task. (See *Assessment Guide* for more information.)

**Writing About Reading Scoring Key**

**0** Reflects **no** understanding of the text.

**1** Reflects **very limited** understanding of the text.

**2** Reflects **partial** understanding of the text.

**3** Reflects **excellent** understanding of the text.

Student _____     Date _____

# Write about three interesting things you learned about koalas. You can draw a picture to go with your writing.

© 2008 by Irene C. Fountas and Gay Su Pinnell. Portsmouth, NH: Heinemann. This page may be photocopied.

Recording Forms

Student _____     Grade _____     Date _____

Teacher _____     School _____

## Recording Form

### Part One: Oral Reading

Place the book in front of the student. Read the title and introduction.

*Introduction*:    Ben's family and the other families on the street got a note from their new neighbors. In the note their new neighbors invited them to see their surprise horses. Read to find out what kind of horses they were.

Sources of Information Used

| Page | Start Time ____ min. ____ sec.          *Our New Neighbors* Level J, RW: 224 | E | SC | E | | | SC | | |
|---|---|---|---|---|---|---|---|---|---|
| | | | | M | S | V | M | S | V |
| 2 | On Saturday morning, Ben saw an envelope on the front steps. "Mom, Dad, Polly!" he called. "Look what I found!" | | | | | | | | |
| 3 | Dad read the note that was inside. Hello Neighbors, We just moved into the big house on the corner. Please come to a party next Saturday at 10 | | | | | | | | |
| | **Subtotal** | | | | | | | | |

**Part One: Oral Reading** *continued*

Sources of Information Used

| Page | Text | E | SC | E | | | SC | | |
|------|------|---|----|---|---|---|----|---|---|
| | | | | M | S | V | M | S | V |
| **3** *cont.* | o'clock. We want to<br><br>meet you <u>and</u> we want<br><br>you to meet our horses.<br><br>Max and Flo | | | | | | | | |
| **4** | "Horses?" Everyone looked at<br><br>one another.<br><br>"Horses on our street?" asked Dad. | | | | | | | | |
| **5** | "I hope they're ponies," said Ben.<br>"When we have birthday parties, we<br><br>can have pony rides."<br><br><br>"I hope they're big white horses," said<br><br>Polly. "Maybe they'll give us a ride." | | | | | | | | |
| | **Subtotal** | | | | | | | | |

**Part One: Oral Reading** *continued*

Sources of Information Used

| Page | Text | E | SC | E | | | SC | | |
|------|------|---|----|---|---|---|----|---|---|
| | | | | M | S | V | M | S | V |
| 6 | "Well," said Mom, "that house on the corner is just right for horses. It has a big yard. And there's that red barn in back." | | | | | | | | |
| 7 | "Look," said Ben. "The neighbors are reading a note, too!" Mom and Dad called across the street. "Did you get the note about the horses?" Dad asked. | | | | | | | | |
| 8 | "What do you think it's all about?" Mom asked the neighbor. | | | | | | | | |
| | **Subtotal** | | | | | | | | |

Recording Forms

## Part One: Oral Reading *continued*

Sources of Information Used

| Page | Text | E | SC | E | | | SC | | |
|------|------|---|-----|---|---|---|---|---|---|
| | | | | M | S | V | M | S | V |
| **8** *cont.* | "I don't know," he said. "I don't think that barn is big enough for horses." | | | | | | | | |
| **9** | Another neighbor popped her head over the fence. "I can tell you something else," she said. "Every day when I pass that house, I hear loud noises, like someone is hammering." All the neighbors were excited about the mystery. | | | | | | | | |
| | Subtotal | | | | | | | | |
| | End Time ___ min. ___ sec.    Total | | | | | | | | |

Have the student finish reading the book silently.

© 2008 by Irene C. Fountas and Gay Su Pinnell. Portsmouth, NH: Heinemann. This page may be photocopied.

Recording Forms

| **Accuracy Rate** | **Errors** | 24 or more | 22–23 | 20–21 | 17–19 | 15–16 | 13–14 | 11–12 | 8–10 | 6–7 | 4–5 | 1–3 | 0 |
|---|---|---|---|---|---|---|---|---|---|---|---|---|---|
| | **%** | Below 90% | 90% | 91% | 92% | 93% | 94% | 95% | 96% | 97% | 98% | 99% | 100% |

**Self-Correction Ratio**

(E + SC) ÷ SC = 1: _____

**Fluency Score**    0    1    2    3

**Fluency Scoring Key**

**0**   Reads primarily word-by-word with occasional but infrequent or inappropriate phrasing; no smooth or expressive interpretation, irregular pausing, and no attention to author's meaning or punctuation; no stress or inappropriate stress, and slow rate.

**1**   Reads primarily in two-word phrases with some three- and four-word groups and some word-by-word reading; almost no smooth, expressive interpretation or pausing guided by author's meaning and punctuation; almost no stress or inappropriate stress, with slow rate most of the time.

**2**   Reads primarily in three- or four-word phrase groups; some smooth, expressive interpretation and pausing guided by author's meaning and punctuation; mostly appropriate stress and rate with some slowdowns.

**3**   Reads primarily in larger, meaningful phrases or word groups; mostly smooth, expressive interpretation and pausing guided by author's meaning and punctuation; appropriate stress and rate with only a few slowdowns.

**Reading Rate**
*(Optional)*

End Time        _____ min. _____ sec.
Start Time      _____ min. _____ sec.
Total Time      _____ min. _____ sec.
Total Seconds   _____

(RW × 60) ÷ Total Seconds = Words Per Minute (WPM)

13,440 ÷ _____ = _____ WPM

Recording Forms

## Part Two: Comprehension Conversation

Have a conversation with the student, noting the key understandings the student expresses. Use prompts as needed to stimulate discussion of understandings the student does not express. Score for evidence of all understandings expressed—with or without a prompt. Circle the number in the score column that reflects the level of understanding demonstrated.

*Teacher:*   Talk about what happened in this story.

**Comprehension Scoring Key**

**0**   Reflects **no** understanding of the text. Either does not respond or talks off the topic.

**1**   Reflects **very limited** understanding of the text. Mentions a few facts or ideas but does not express the important information or ideas.

**2**   Reflects **partial** understanding of the text. Includes important information and ideas but neglects other key understandings.

**3**   Reflects **excellent** understanding of the text. Includes almost all important information and main ideas.

| Key Understandings | Prompts | Score |
|---|---|---|
| **Within the Text**<br><br>Recounts most of the important events such as: the new neighbors invited everyone to see their horses; everyone was asking what kind of horses the neighbors had; the horses turned out to be a merry-go-round (or carousel).<br><br>*Note any additional understandings:* | What was the mystery in the story?<br><br>What did the new neighbors do to get everyone interested in their horses?<br><br>What happened when people got the note?<br><br>What happened at the end? | 0  1  2  3 |
| **Beyond the Text**<br><br>The new neighbors wanted to surprise everyone so they kept the horses a secret.<br><br>Everyone was wondering about the horses and imagining the kinds of horses they were.<br><br>Clues before the last page are: "loud hammering noises," "music playing," "two horses going up and two going down," "four horses going around and around."<br><br>*Note any additional understandings:* | Why did the new neighbors keep the horses a secret?<br><br>What were the people in the neighborhood thinking about the horses?<br><br>There were a few clues that might have helped you guess what kind of horses were in the barn. Can you think of any? | 0  1  2  3 |

*Continued on next page.*

## Part Two: Comprehension Conversation *continued*

### Guide to Total Score

| | |
|---|---|
| 6–7 | **Excellent** Comprehension |
| 5 | **Satisfactory** Comprehension |
| 4 | **Limited** Comprehension |
| 0–3 | **Unsatisfactory** Comprehension |

Subtotal Score: _____ /6

Add 1 for any additional understandings: _____ /1

Total Score: _____ /7

## Part Three: Writing About Reading *(optional)*

Read the writing/drawing prompt on the next page to the student. Specify the amount of time for the student to complete the task. (See *Assessment Guide* for more information.)

### Writing About Reading Scoring Key

**0** Reflects **no** understanding of the text.

**1** Reflects **very limited** understanding of the text.

**2** Reflects **partial** understanding of the text.

**3** Reflects **excellent** understanding of the text.

Student _____     Date _____

Write about the horses and how the new neighbors made them a surprise for everyone. You can draw a picture to go with your writing.

Student _____    Grade _____    Date _____

Teacher _____    School _____

## Recording Form
### Part One: Oral Reading

Place the book in front of the student. Read the title and introduction.

*Introduction*:    Dogs can be more than pets. They can help people. Therapy dogs help people feel better and service dogs help people do things. Read to find out about these two kinds of dogs and what they do.

Sources of Information Used

| Page | Start Time ____ min. ____ sec. | *More Than a Pet* Level J, RW: 263 | E | SC | E M | E S | E V | SC M | SC S | SC V |
|------|---|---|---|---|---|---|---|---|---|---|
| 2 | Do you know anyone who has a pet dog? Maybe you have a dog in your family. Dogs are good pets. | | | | | | | | | |
| 3 | Some dogs are more than pets. Two kinds of dogs do special jobs. Dogs that make people feel better are called **therapy dogs**. Dogs that work are called **service dogs**. | | | | | | | | | |
| | | **Subtotal** | | | | | | | | |

**Part One: Oral Reading** *continued*

Sources of Information Used

| Page | Text | E | SC | E | | | SC | | |
|------|------|---|----|---|---|---|----|---|---|
| | | | | M | S | V | M | S | V |
| 4 | [Therapy Dogs]<br><br>Sometimes people can not<br><br>stay at home because they<br><br>are not well. They must<br><br>stay in a hospital or in<br><br>a nursing home. They miss<br><br>their homes and families.<br><br>People feel better<br><br>when they pet a dog. | | | | | | | | |
| 7 | People like to pet dogs<br><br>and feel their soft fur.<br><br>Therapy dogs cheer people up<br><br>when they are sad because<br><br>they are not feeling well. | | | | | | | | |
| | **Subtotal** | | | | | | | | |

**Part One: Oral Reading** *continued*

Sources of Information Used

| Page | Text | E | SC | E | | | SC | | |
|------|------|---|----|---|---|---|----|---|---|
| | | | | M | S | V | M | S | V |
| 8 | May is a friendly and snuggly dog. She visits Sam in the hospital. She curls right up in bed, and Sam smiles. | | | | | | | | |
| 9 | Addie is a gentle pup. Her owner takes her to visit people in a nursing home. She stays very still when they pet her. | | | | | | | | |
| 10 | [Service Dogs] Service dogs are more than pets. Service dogs live with the people they help. | | | | | | | | |
| | Subtotal | | | | | | | | |

**Part One: Oral Reading** *continued*

Sources of Information Used

| Page | Text | E | SC | E | | | SC | | |
|------|------|---|----|---|---|---|----|---|---|
| | | | | M | S | V | M | S | V |
| **10** *cont.* | They work, play, and go everywhere with their owners. | | | | | | | | |
| **11** | Service dogs go to a special school where they are trained to help their owners. | | | | | | | | |
| **12** | Royal is a service dog who helps Lily, his owner. Lily needs help because she can't see well. Royal came to live with Lily when he was a puppy. He and Lily were trained together. | | | | | | | | |
| | **Subtotal** | | | | | | | | |

**Part One: Oral Reading** *continued*

Sources of Information Used

| Page | Text | E | SC | E | | | SC | | |
|------|------|---|----|---|---|---|----|---|---|
| | | | | M | S | V | M | S | V |
| **12** *cont.* | Now, Royal and Lily<br><br>are together all the time.<br><br>Lily holds on to Royal's harness<br><br>at the mall or on the train.<br><br>Royal makes sure it's safe<br><br>for Lily to walk. | | | | | | | | |
| | **Subtotal** | | | | | | | | |
| | End Time _____ min. _____ sec.     **Total** | | | | | | | | |

Have the student finish reading the book silently.

© 2008 by Irene C. Fountas and Gay Su Pinnell. Portsmouth, NH: Heinemann. This page may be photocopied.

| Accuracy Rate | Errors | 28 or more | 25–27 | 23–24 | 20–22 | 18–19 | 15–17 | 12–14 | 10–11 | 7–9 | 4–6 | 1–3 | 0 |
|---|---|---|---|---|---|---|---|---|---|---|---|---|---|
| | % | Below 90% | 90% | 91% | 92% | 93% | 94% | 95% | 96% | 97% | 98% | 99% | 100% |

| Self-Correction Ratio | (E + SC) ÷ SC = 1: _____ |
|---|---|

**Fluency Score**    0    1    2    3

**Fluency Scoring Key**

**0** Reads primarily word-by-word with occasional but infrequent or inappropriate phrasing; no smooth or expressive interpretation, irregular pausing, and no attention to author's meaning or punctuation; no stress or inappropriate stress, and slow rate.

**1** Reads primarily in two-word phrases with some three- and four-word groups and some word-by-word reading; almost no smooth, expressive interpretation or pausing guided by author's meaning and punctuation; almost no stress or inappropriate stress, with slow rate most of the time.

**2** Reads primarily in three- or four-word phrase groups; some smooth, expressive interpretation and pausing guided by author's meaning and punctuation; mostly appropriate stress and rate with some slowdowns.

**3** Reads primarily in larger, meaningful phrases or word groups; mostly smooth, expressive interpretation and pausing guided by author's meaning and punctuation; appropriate stress and rate with only a few slowdowns.

## Part Two: Comprehension Conversation

Have a conversation with the student, noting the key understandings the student expresses. Use prompts as needed to stimulate discussion of understandings the student does not express. Score for evidence of all understandings expressed—with or without a prompt. Circle the number in the score column that reflects the level of understanding demonstrated.

*Teacher:*    Talk about what you learned in this book.

| **Comprehension Scoring Key** |
| --- |
| **0**   Reflects **no** understanding of the text. Either does not respond or talks off the topic. |
| **1**   Reflects **very limited** understanding of the text. Mentions a few facts or ideas but does not express the important information or ideas. |
| **2**   Reflects **partial** understanding of the text. Includes important information and ideas but neglects other key understandings. |
| **3**   Reflects **excellent** understanding of the text. Includes almost all important information and main ideas. |

| Key Understandings | Prompts | Score |
| --- | --- | --- |
| **Within the Text**<br><br>There are two kinds of dogs that help people. Some dogs help people feel better and some dogs work. (May or may not use the terms *therapy* and *service*.)<br><br>Dogs help people in many different ways. (Gives 2–3 examples such as: dogs cheer people up; they help their owners; they make sure the owner is safe; they get things for their owners.)<br><br>*Note any additional understandings:* | What were the two kinds of dogs that you read about?<br><br>What did you learn about therapy dogs?<br><br>What did you learn about service dogs?<br><br>What else did you learn about the two kinds of dogs? | 0   1   2   3 |
| **Beyond the Text**<br><br>I didn't know that (gives examples of new information).<br><br>Dogs must be smart because they can learn to help people in different ways (or people train them).<br><br>Dogs are good pets and they can also do a lot more things to help people.<br><br>In this picture, the woman is blind and the dog is helping her get on a train.<br><br>*Note any additional understandings:* | What new information did you learn about dogs when you read this book?<br><br>Why do you think dogs can be so helpful?<br><br>Why do you think dogs are so important to people?<br><br>Look at the photograph on page 13. What information does it give you? | 0   1   2   3 |

| **Guide to Total Score** |
| --- |
| **6–7**   **Excellent** Comprehension |
| **5**   **Satisfactory** Comprehension |
| **4**   **Limited** Comprehension |
| **0–3**   **Unsatisfactory** Comprehension |

Subtotal Score: _____ /6

Add 1 for any additional understandings: _____ /1

Total Score: _____ /7

## Part Three: Writing About Reading *(optional)*

Read the writing/drawing prompt on the next page to the student. Specify the amount of time for the student to complete the task. (See *Assessment Guide* for more information.)

**Writing About Reading Scoring Key**

**0** Reflects **no** understanding of the text.

**1** Reflects **very limited** understanding of the text.

**2** Reflects **partial** understanding of the text.

**3** Reflects **excellent** understanding of the text.

Student _____     Date _____

Write about three ways dogs help people. You can draw a picture to go with your writing.

Recording Forms

**Student** _____  **Grade** _____  **Date** _____

**Teacher** _____  **School** _____

## Recording Form

### Part One: Oral Reading

Place the book in front of the student. Read the title and introduction.

*Introduction*: Edwin's hair was so long that he looked like his dog Ruff. His mom and dad gave him a haircut, and it was so bad he had to wear a wig hat. Read to find out what happened.

Sources of Information Used

| Page | Start Time ____ min. ____ sec.  *Edwin's Haircut* Level K, RW: 234 | E | SC | E | | | SC | | |
|---|---|---|---|---|---|---|---|---|---|
| | | | | M | S | V | M | S | V |
| 2 | "Good morning, Edwin," Dad said. He was talking to Edwin's dog, Ruff. Then he turned to Edwin. "Good morning, Ruff," he said to his shaggy son. | | | | | | | | |
| 3 | He could tell that his dad was only joking, but Edwin did not laugh or smile. Instead, he pushed his hair off his face and said, "I'm not Ruff. I'm EDWIN! See? Ruff is the one with the tail." | | | | | | | | |
| | **Subtotal** | | | | | | | | |

© 2008 by Irene C. Fountas and Gay Su Pinnell. Portsmouth, NH: Heinemann. This page may be photocopied.

Recording Forms

**Part One: Oral Reading** *continued*

Sources of Information Used

| Page | Text | E | SC | E | | | SC | | |
|------|------|---|-----|---|---|---|-----|---|---|
| | | | | M | S | V | M | S | V |
| **3**<br>*cont.* | "Why, I think you are right," answered Dad. "I don't know how I could have mixed you up with Ruff."<br><br>"I know how," said Mom. "It's time for a haircut!" | | | | | | | | |
| **4** | Mom put some newspapers on the floor and sat Edwin in a chair. Then she was ready to cut Edwin's hair. | | | | | | | | |
| **5** | Snip! Mom took a little off the top.<br><br>Snip! She took some off the back.<br><br>Then she cut a lot off the sides.<br><br>"It doesn't look right," said Dad. "One side is too long. Let me try."<br><br>Snip! went Dad. | | | | | | | | |
| | **Subtotal** | | | | | | | | |

## Part One: Oral Reading *continued*

Sources of Information Used

| Page | Text | E | SC | E | | | SC | | |
|------|------|---|----|---|---|---|----|---|---|
| | | | | M | S | V | M | S | V |
| 6 | "Now the other side is too long," Mom complained. "Let's see if I can fix it." Snip! Snip! "It's still not right," said Dad. "Let me take a bit more off this side." | | | | | | | | |
| 7 | Edwin's mom and dad took turns snipping and trimming, but the more they snipped, the worse things got. Edwin's hair got more and more crooked. "We'd better quit," said Mom. Dad agreed. "If we don't, he's not going to have any hair left!" he said. | | | | | | | | |
| | **Subtotal** | | | | | | | | |
| | End Time ____ min. ____ sec.     **Total** | | | | | | | | |

Have the student finish reading the book silently.

| | **Errors** | 25 or more | 23–24 | 20–22 | 18–19 | 16–17 | 13–15 | 11–12 | 9–10 | 6–8 | 4–5 | 1–3 | 0 |
|---|---|---|---|---|---|---|---|---|---|---|---|---|---|
| **Accuracy Rate** | **%** | Below 90% | 90% | 91% | 92% | 93% | 94% | 95% | 96% | 97% | 98% | 99% | 100% |

| **Self-Correction Ratio** | (E + SC) ÷ SC = 1: ____ |
|---|---|

| **Fluency Score** | 0   1   2   3 | **Fluency Scoring Key** |
|---|---|---|

**Fluency Scoring Key**

**0**  Reads primarily word-by-word with occasional but infrequent or inappropriate phrasing; no smooth or expressive interpretation, irregular pausing, and no attention to author's meaning or punctuation; no stress or inappropriate stress, and slow rate.

**1**  Reads primarily in two-word phrases with some three- and four-word groups and some word-by-word reading; almost no smooth, expressive interpretation or pausing guided by author's meaning and punctuation; almost no stress or inappropriate stress, with slow rate most of the time.

**2**  Reads primarily in three- or four-word phrase groups; some smooth, expressive interpretation and pausing guided by author's meaning and punctuation; mostly appropriate stress and rate with some slowdowns.

**3**  Reads primarily in larger, meaningful phrases or word groups; mostly smooth, expressive interpretation and pausing guided by author's meaning and punctuation; appropriate stress and rate with only a few slowdowns.

## Part Two: Comprehension Conversation

Have a conversation with the student, noting the key understandings the student expresses. Use prompts as needed to stimulate discussion of understandings the student does not express. Score for evidence of all understandings expressed—with or without a prompt. Circle the number in the score column that reflects the level of understanding demonstrated.

*Teacher:*    Talk about what happened in this story.

**Comprehension Scoring Key**

**0**   Reflects **no** understanding of the text. Either does not respond or talks off the topic.

**1**   Reflects **very limited** understanding of the text. Mentions a few facts or ideas but does not express the important information or ideas.

**2**   Reflects **partial** understanding of the text. Includes important information and ideas but neglects other key understandings.

**3**   Reflects **excellent** understanding of the text. Includes almost all important information and main ideas.

| Key Understandings | Prompts | Score |
|---|---|---|
| **Within the Text**<br><br>Edwin got a terrible haircut and had to wear a wig hat (or wig) all of the time.<br><br>Recounts most of the important events such as: Edwin needed a haircut so his mom and dad gave him one; his hair looked awful; he had to wear a wig hat everywhere; his hair grew out again but he wouldn't let his mom cut it; he said that next time he would pick the barber to give him his haircut.<br><br>*Note any additional understandings:* | What was the problem in this story?<br><br>How did Edwin and his parents solve the problem?<br><br>What happened at the end? | 0  1  2  3 |
| **Beyond the Text**<br><br>Edwin hated his haircut. It was so bad that he was embarrassed to go to school.<br><br>Edwin didn't care if other kids teased him about his wig hat. He just went on and did everything he always did.<br><br>Edwin stuck up for himself in the end when he said he would pick the barber next time.<br><br>The beginning and ending of the story were alike because he needed a haircut, but in the end Edwin changed his mind about who should cut his hair.<br><br>*Note any additional understandings:* | How do you think Edwin felt when he first looked at himself with his new haircut?<br><br>What kind of kid was Edwin? What was he like? What makes you think that?<br><br>Edwin acted differently at the end of the story than he did at the beginning. What did he do that was different?<br><br>How were the beginning and ending parts of this story alike? How were they different? | 0  1  2  3 |

*Continued on next page.*

Recording Forms

## Part Two: Comprehension Conversation *continued*

| Guide to Total Score | |
|---|---|
| 6–7 | **Excellent** Comprehension |
| 5 | **Satisfactory** Comprehension |
| 4 | **Limited** Comprehension |
| 0–3 | **Unsatisfactory** Comprehension |

Subtotal Score: _____ /6

Add 1 for any additional understandings: _____ /1

Total Score: _____ /7

## Part Three: Writing About Reading *(optional)*

Read the writing/drawing prompt on the next page to the student. Specify the amount of time for the student to complete the task. (See *Assessment Guide* for more information.)

**Writing About Reading Scoring Key**
0 Reflects **no** understanding of the text.
1 Reflects **very limited** understanding of the text.
2 Reflects **partial** understanding of the text.
3 Reflects **excellent** understanding of the text.

Student _____ Date _____

At the end of the story, Edwin decided to have his hair cut by a barber. Do you think this was a good idea? Write about why or why not. You can draw a picture to go with your writing.

Recording Forms

Student _____    Grade _____    Date _____

Teacher _____    School _____

## Recording Form

### Part One: Oral Reading

Place the book in front of the student. Read the title and introduction.

*Introduction*:    Animals and people have five senses. But animal senses do not always work like people's senses work. Read to find out how some animals see, touch, taste, smell, and hear.

Sources of Information Used

| Page | Start Time ____ min. ____ sec.      *Surprising Animal Senses* Level K, RW: 266 | E | SC | E | | | SC | | |
|---|---|---|---|---|---|---|---|---|---|
| | | | | M | S | V | M | S | V |
| 2 | [Introduction]<br><br>You may already know about your five senses. People can see, touch, taste, smell, and hear.<br><br>Animals also use their senses to learn about the world. But animal senses do not always work the way people's senses work.<br><br>In this book you will read about how animal senses work—how many animals see, touch, taste, smell, and hear in ways that are different from people. | | | | | | | | |
| | **Subtotal** | | | | | | | | |

**Part One: Oral Reading** *continued*

Sources of Information Used

| Page | Text | E | SC | E | | | SC | | |
|------|------|---|----|---|---|---|----|---|---|
| | | | | M | S | V | M | S | V |
| 4 | [Sight]<br><br>Who is the mother and who is the child in this picture? How can you tell?<br><br>You use your sense of sight. | | | | | | | | |
| 5 | You use your eyes to see. A starfish uses its arms! Starfish do not have eyes. Instead, they have small spots at the ends of their arms to help them see light and dark. | | | | | | | | |
| 6 | [Touch]<br><br>If your eyes are closed, how can you tell the difference between a soft chick and rough sandpaper? You use your sense of touch. | | | | | | | | |
| | **Subtotal** | | | | | | | | |

Recording Forms

## Part One: Oral Reading *continued*

Sources of Information Used

| Page | Text | E | SC | E | | | SC | | |
|---|---|---|---|---|---|---|---|---|---|
| | | | | M | S | V | M | S | V |
| 7 | You use your skin to touch. Cats do, too. But cats also use their whiskers! The touch of the whiskers helps cats know whether they can fit through small openings. | | | | | | | | |
| 8 | [Taste]<br><br>How can you tell if you like salad?<br>You use your sense of taste. | | | | | | | | |
| 9 | You use your tongue to taste. A butterfly tastes with its feet! When butterflies land on flowers, they use taste buds on their feet to know if the flowers are good to eat. | | | | | | | | |
| | Subtotal | | | | | | | | |

**Part One: Oral Reading** *continued*

Sources of Information Used

| Page | Text | E | SC | E | | | SC | | |
|---|---|---|---|---|---|---|---|---|---|
| | | | | M | S | V | M | S | V |
| 10 | [Smell]<br><br>Do you like the smell of fresh flowers? Most people do. Your sense of smell tells you that flowers smell good. | | | | | | | | |
| 11 | You use your nose to smell. Snakes use their mouths! Instead of sniffing, they flick their tongues to bring smells into their mouths. | | | | | | | | |
| | **Subtotal** | | | | | | | | |
| | **End Time** ____ min. ____ sec.　　**Total** | | | | | | | | |

Have the student finish reading the book silently.

Recording Forms

| Accuracy Rate | Errors | 28 or more | 26–27 | 23–25 | 20–22 | 18–19 | 15–17 | 12–14 | 10–11 | 7–9 | 5–6 | 1–4 | 0 |
|---|---|---|---|---|---|---|---|---|---|---|---|---|---|
| | % | Below 90% | 90% | 91% | 92% | 93% | 94% | 95% | 96% | 97% | 98% | 99% | 100% |

**Self-Correction Ratio**

$(E + SC) \div SC = 1:\underline{\hspace{1cm}}$

**Fluency Score**    0    1    2    3

**Fluency Scoring Key**

**0**  Reads primarily word-by-word with occasional but infrequent or inappropriate phrasing; no smooth or expressive interpretation, irregular pausing, and no attention to author's meaning or punctuation; no stress or inappropriate stress, and slow rate.

**1**  Reads primarily in two-word phrases with some three- and four-word groups and some word-by-word reading; almost no smooth, expressive interpretation or pausing guided by author's meaning and punctuation; almost no stress or inappropriate stress, with slow rate most of the time.

**2**  Reads primarily in three- or four-word phrase groups; some smooth, expressive interpretation and pausing guided by author's meaning and punctuation; mostly appropriate stress and rate with some slowdowns.

**3**  Reads primarily in larger, meaningful phrases or word groups; mostly smooth, expressive interpretation and pausing guided by author's meaning and punctuation; appropriate stress and rate with only a few slowdowns.

**Reading Rate** *(Optional)*

End Time        _____ min. _____ sec.

Start Time      _____ min. _____ sec.

Total Time      _____ min. _____ sec.

Total Seconds   _____

(RW × 60) ÷ Total Seconds = Words Per Minute (WPM)

15,960 ÷ _____ = _____ WPM

## Part Two: Comprehension Conversation

Have a conversation with the student, noting the key understandings the student expresses. Use prompts as needed to stimulate discussion of understandings the student does not express. Score for evidence of all understandings expressed—with or without a prompt. Circle the number in the score column that reflects the level of understanding demonstrated.

*Teacher:*    Talk about what you learned in this book.

---

**Comprehension Scoring Key**

**0**   Reflects **no** understanding of the text. Either does not respond or talks off the topic.

**1**   Reflects **very limited** understanding of the text. Mentions a few facts or ideas but does not express the important information or ideas.

**2**   Reflects **partial** understanding of the text. Includes important information and ideas but neglects other key understandings.

**3**   Reflects **excellent** understanding of the text. Includes almost all important information and main ideas.

---

| Key Understandings | Prompts | Score |
|---|---|---|
| **Within the Text**<br><br>People and animals have senses.<br><br>Some animals use their senses in different ways than people.<br><br>Reports 2–3 details about how animals use their senses such as: a starfish uses its arms to see; a cat uses its whiskers to feel; a butterfly uses its feet to taste; a snake uses its tongue to smell; a cricket uses its front legs to hear; some animals have super senses that are stronger than people's.<br><br>*Note any additional understandings:* | What did you learn about animals and their senses?<br><br>Are animals' senses the same as people's senses?<br><br>How do some animals use their senses? How else? Tell about some examples from this book. | 0  1  2  3 |
| **Beyond the Text**<br><br>Reports one cause/effect relationship such as, dogs are good at tracking people because they can smell a million times better than people.<br><br>Animals can do things people cannot do because of their senses. (Gives an example such as: birds can see from high in the sky; bloodhounds can track a person's smell; bats can listen to know where they are in the dark.)<br><br>The heading "Super Senses" means that all these animals have a super sense of some kind that is stronger than ours.<br><br>*Note any additional understandings:* | Why do animals need these special senses?<br><br>Can animals' senses help them do things people cannot do? How? What is an example?<br><br>Look at the heading on page 14. What does this heading tell you about the information in this section? | 0  1  2  3 |

*Continued on next page.*

## Part Two: Comprehension Conversation *continued*

**Guide to Total Score**

| | |
|---|---|
| 6–7 | **Excellent** Comprehension |
| 5 | **Satisfactory** Comprehension |
| 4 | **Limited** Comprehension |
| 0–3 | **Unsatisfactory** Comprehension |

Subtotal Score: _____ /6

Add 1 for any additional understandings: _____ /1

Total Score: _____ /7

## Part Three: Writing About Reading *(optional)*

Read the writing/drawing prompt on the next page to the student. Specify the amount of time for the student to complete the task. (See *Assessment Guide* for more information.)

**Writing About Reading Scoring Key**

**0** Reflects **no** understanding of the text.

**1** Reflects **very limited** understanding of the text.

**2** Reflects **partial** understanding of the text.

**3** Reflects **excellent** understanding of the text.

Recording Forms

Student _____     Date _____

Write about three animals and how they use their senses. You can draw a picture to go with your writing.

Student _____   Grade _____   Date _____

Teacher _____   School _____

## Recording Form
### Part One: Oral Reading

Place the book in front of the student. Read the title and introduction.

*Introduction*:   April was reading a book about a dog who rescued a man. She decided to write a letter to her favorite author, Julia Reed. She wanted the author to write a book about her dog, Golden Boy. Read to find out what happened.

Sources of Information Used

| Page | Start Time ____ min. ____ sec.    *Dog Stories* Level L, RW: 267 | E | SC | E | | | SC | | |
|------|---|---|---|---|---|---|---|---|---|
| | | | | M | S | V | M | S | V |
| 2 | April Bailey was reading to her dog, Golden Boy. Her voice got more excited as she read the last few lines. | | | | | | | | |
| 3 | *"Roxy to the Rescue* is the best book ever!" April told Golden Boy. April was always having Big Ideas, and she had one right then and there. | | | | | | | | |
| 4 | "I'm going to write a letter to Julia Reed to tell her how much I love this book," April said. | | | | | | | | |
| | Subtotal | | | | | | | | |

**Part One: Oral Reading** *continued*

Sources of Information Used

| Page | Text | E | SC | E | | | SC | | |
|------|------|---|----|---|---|---|----|---|---|
| | | | | M | S | V | M | S | V |
| **4** *cont.* | "Who's Julia Reed?" her brother Scott asked. | | | | | | | | |
| **5** | "She's my favorite author," April said. "All of her books are about dogs, right, Golden Boy?" | | | | | | | | |
| **6** | April finished her letter and read it out loud. Golden Boy turned his head. He seemed to be listening. | | | | | | | | |
| **7** | November 8 Dear Ms. Reed, *Roxy to the Rescue* is your best book yet! | | | | | | | | |
| | **Subtotal** | | | | | | | | |

Recording Forms

**Part One: Oral Reading** *continued*

Sources of Information Used

| Page | Text | E | SC | E | | | SC | | |
|------|------|---|----|---|---|---|----|---|---|
| | | | | M | S | V | M | S | V |
| **7** *cont.* | I have a Lab named Golden Boy. He's super smart, and he is a super-sniffer! Please would you write about Golden Boy next? He would be a wonderful dog hero. Your biggest fan, April Bailey | | | | | | | | |
| **8** | April put a photograph of Golden Boy in the envelope, along with her letter. "Hey, don't get your hopes up," warned Scott. "She may get a zillion letters a day." | | | | | | | | |
| | **Subtotal** | | | | | | | | |

## Part One: Oral Reading *continued*

Sources of Information Used

| Page | Text | E | SC | E | | | SC | | |
|------|------|---|----|---|---|---|----|---|---|
| | | | | M | S | V | M | S | V |
| 9 | "I just know Julia Reed will answer me," April said. "She's a dog lover, just like me." She stuck a stamp on the envelope. It was a dog stamp, of course! | | | | | | | | |
| 10 | "Find your leash, Boy," April told her dog. "Let's go mail this letter." Golden Boy put his nose to the floor, sniffing. Then he dove behind a chair. When he came back out, the missing leash was dangling from his mouth. "That's my super-sniffer!" April said. | | | | | | | | |
| | **Subtotal** | | | | | | | | |
| | End Time ____ min. ____ sec.  **Total** | | | | | | | | |

Have the student finish reading the book silently.

Recording Forms

| | **Errors** | **15 or more** | **13–14** | **10–12** | **7–9** | **5–6** | **1–4** |
|---|---|---|---|---|---|---|---|
| **Accuracy Rate** | **%** | Below 95% | 95% | 96% | 97% | 98% | 99% |

**Self-Correction Ratio**

$$(E + SC) \div SC = 1:\underline{\hspace{1cm}}$$

**Fluency Score**

0   1   2   3

**Fluency Scoring Key**

**0**  Reads primarily word-by-word with occasional but infrequent or inappropriate phrasing; no smooth or expressive interpretation, irregular pausing, and no attention to author's meaning or punctuation; no stress or inappropriate stress, and slow rate.

**1**  Reads primarily in two-word phrases with some three- and four-word groups and some word-by-word reading; almost no smooth, expressive interpretation or pausing guided by author's meaning and punctuation; almost no stress or inappropriate stress, with slow rate most of the time.

**2**  Reads primarily in three- or four-word phrase groups; some smooth, expressive interpretation and pausing guided by author's meaning and punctuation; mostly appropriate stress and rate with some slowdowns.

**3**  Reads primarily in larger, meaningful phrases or word groups; mostly smooth, expressive interpretation and pausing guided by author's meaning and punctuation; appropriate stress and rate with only a few slowdowns.

**Reading Rate**
*(Optional)*

End Time        _____ min. _____ sec.

Start Time      _____ min. _____ sec.

Total Time      _____ min. _____ sec.

Total Seconds   _____

(RW × 60) ÷ Total Seconds = Words Per Minute (WPM)

16,020 ÷ _____ = _____ WPM

## Part Two: Comprehension Conversation

Have a conversation with the student, noting the key understandings the student expresses. Use prompts as needed to stimulate discussion of understandings the student does not express. Score for evidence of all understandings expressed—with or without a prompt. Circle the number in the score column that reflects the level of understanding demonstrated.

*Teacher*:   Talk about what happened in this story.

**Comprehension Scoring Key**

**0**   Reflects **no** understanding of the text. Either does not respond or talks off the topic.

**1**   Reflects **very limited** understanding of the text. Mentions a few facts or ideas but does not express the important information or ideas.

**2**   Reflects **partial** understanding of the text. Includes important information and ideas but neglects other key understandings.

**3**   Reflects **excellent** understanding of the text. Includes almost all important information and main ideas.

| Key Understandings | Prompts | Score |
|---|---|---|
| **Within the Text**<br><br>Recounts the most important story events, such as: April was reading to her dog; she wanted her favorite author to write a story about Golden Boy; she wrote a letter to Julia Reed (or the writer) and got one back; April started to write her own story.<br><br>*Note any additional understandings:* | What happened in this story? Then what happened?<br><br>What happened at the end? | 0   1   2   3 |
| **Beyond the Text**<br><br>April likes to read and write. She likes authors and stories. She likes her dog.<br><br>She loved her dog, Golden Boy, so she wanted a book written about him.<br><br>April learned that when you write about a dog, you have to know the dog. She learned that she could write the book about her dog and be a good author.<br><br>*Note any additional understandings:* | Tell what you learned about April. What does she like to do?<br><br>Why did April want her favorite author to write a story about Golden Boy?<br><br>April learned a lesson about being a writer. What do you think she learned? | 0   1   2   3 |

*Continued on next page.*

Recording Forms

## Part Two: Comprehension Conversation *continued*

| Key Understandings | Prompts | Score |
|---|---|---|
| **About the Text**<br><br>In this book there are letters from people, a story, and a page from a book.<br><br>April wrote a good letter to the author (and tells why the letter was good.)<br><br>The letter she got from Julia Reed is probably what a writer would really say.<br><br>*Note any additional understandings:* | This book had different kinds of writing in it, didn't it? What were the different kinds of writing?<br><br>Did you think April wrote a good letter to Julia Reed? Why (not)?<br><br>Do you think what happened in *Dog Stories* could really happen? Why (not)? | 0   1   2   3 |

**Guide to Total Score**

**9–10 Excellent** Comprehension

**7–8 Satisfactory** Comprehension

**5–6 Limited** Comprehension

**0–4 Unsatisfactory** Comprehension

Subtotal Score: _____ /9

Add 1 for any additional understandings: _____ /1

Total Score: _____ /10

---

## Part Three: Writing About Reading *(optional)*

Read the writing/drawing prompt on the next page to the student. Specify the amount of time for the student to complete the task. (See *Assessment Guide* for more information.)

**Writing About Reading Scoring Key**

**0** Reflects **no** understanding of the text.

**1** Reflects **very limited** understanding of the text.

**2** Reflects **partial** understanding of the text.

**3** Reflects **excellent** understanding of the text.

Student _____    Date _____

Write about April and what she learned in the story. You can draw a picture to go with your writing.

© 2008 by Irene C. Fountas and Gay Su Pinnell. Portsmouth, NH: Heinemann. This page may be photocopied.

Recording Forms

Recording Forms

Student _____     Grade _____     Date _____

Teacher _____     School _____

## Recording Form

### Part One: Oral Reading

Place the book in front of the student. Read the title and introduction.

*Introduction*:  In this book, you will learn many things about whales, such as what they look like, how they live, how they are born, and where you can see them. Read to learn about the largest animals in the world.

Sources of Information Used

| Page | Start Time _____ min. _____ sec.   *Giants of the Sea* Level L, RW: 268 | E | SC | E | | | SC | | |
|---|---|---|---|---|---|---|---|---|---|
| | | | | M | S | V | M | S | V |
| 2 | [The Largest Animal]<br><br>Think of the biggest animal you know.<br><br>Is it a horse? Is it an elephant?<br><br>The largest animal lives in the sea. It is<br><br>much bigger than a horse or an elephant.<br><br>It is the blue whale, a giant of the sea. | | | | | | | | |
| 3 | The blue whale is the largest animal<br><br>on Earth. | | | | | | | | |
| 4 | Other whales are big, too.<br><br>They may be different colors and | | | | | | | | |
| | **Subtotal** | | | | | | | | |

**Recording Forms**

**Part One: Oral Reading** continued

Sources of Information Used

| Page | Text | E | SC | E M | E S | E V | SC M | SC S | SC V |
|------|------|---|----|----|----|----|----|----|----|
| **4** cont. | different shapes, but they are all very large. | | | | | | | | |
| **6** | [Breathing and Diving] Whales look like fish, but they are not fish. Whales live in the water, but they cannot breathe underwater the way fish can. All whales breathe air. | | | | | | | | |
| **7** | Whales have lungs, like you do. You breathe through your nose or mouth. Whales breathe through holes on the tops of their heads. The holes are called *blowholes*. | | | | | | | | |
| | **Subtotal** | | | | | | | | |

**Part One: Oral Reading** *continued*

Sources of Information Used

| Page | Text | E | SC | E | | | SC | | |
|------|------|---|----|---|---|---|----|---|---|
| | | | | M | S | V | M | S | V |
| 8 | A whale swims up to the top of the water. It blows air out of its blowhole. The whale blows so hard that it makes a cloudy spray called *blow*. | | | | | | | | |
| 9 | Then the whale takes a deep breath. Air goes in through the blowhole. The blowhole snaps shut, and the whale is ready to dive under the water again. Some whales can stay underwater for one hour or more. | | | | | | | | |
| | **Subtotal** | | | | | | | | |

Recording Forms

**Part One: Oral Reading** *continued*

Sources of Information Used

| Page | Text | E | SC | E | | | SC | | |
|------|------|---|----|---|---|---|----|---|---|
| | | | | M | S | V | M | S | V |
| 10 | [Baby Whales]<br><br>A baby whale is called a *calf*. As soon as a calf is born, the mother whale helps it swim up to the surface of the water. Then the newborn calf takes its first breath. | | | | | | | | |
| 11 | A baby whale learns to swim soon after it is born. The calf stays close to its mother for about a year. A whale calf grows fast. A baby blue whale can gain as much as 200 pounds a day! | | | | | | | | |
| | **Subtotal** | | | | | | | | |
| | **End Time** ____ min. ____ sec.     **Total** | | | | | | | | |

Have the student finish reading the book silently.

© 2008 by Irene C. Fountas and Gay Su Pinnell. Portsmouth, NH: Heinemann. This page may be photocopied.

| Accuracy Rate | Errors | 15 or more | 13–14 | 10–12 | 7–9 | 5–6 | 1–4 |
|---|---|---|---|---|---|---|---|
| | % | Below 95% | 95% | 96% | 97% | 98% | 99% |

**Self-Correction Ratio**

(E + SC) ÷ SC = 1: _____

**Fluency Score**    0    1    2    3

**Fluency Scoring Key**

**0**  Reads primarily word-by-word with occasional but infrequent or inappropriate phrasing; no smooth or expressive interpretation, irregular pausing, and no attention to author's meaning or punctuation; no stress or inappropriate stress, and slow rate.

**1**  Reads primarily in two-word phrases with some three- and four-word groups and some word-by-word reading; almost no smooth, expressive interpretation or pausing guided by author's meaning and punctuation; almost no stress or inappropriate stress, with slow rate most of the time.

**2**  Reads primarily in three- or four-word phrase groups; some smooth, expressive interpretation and pausing guided by author's meaning and punctuation; mostly appropriate stress and rate with some slowdowns.

**3**  Reads primarily in larger, meaningful phrases or word groups; mostly smooth, expressive interpretation and pausing guided by author's meaning and punctuation; appropriate stress and rate with only a few slowdowns.

**Reading Rate** *(Optional)*

End Time        _____ min. _____ sec.
Start Time      _____ min. _____ sec.
Total Time      _____ min. _____ sec.
Total Seconds   _____

(RW × 60) ÷ Total Seconds = Words Per Minute (WPM)

16,080 ÷ _____ = _____ WPM

## Part Two: Comprehension Conversation

Have a conversation with the student, noting the key understandings
the student expresses. Use prompts as needed to stimulate discussion of
understandings the student does not express. Score for evidence of all
understandings expressed—with or without a prompt. Circle the number in
the score column that reflects the level of understanding demonstrated.

*Teacher:*   Talk about what you learned in this book.

| **Comprehension Scoring Key** |
| --- |
| **0**   Reflects **no** understanding of the text. Either does not respond or talks off the topic. |
| **1**   Reflects **very limited** understanding of the text. Mentions a few facts or ideas but does not express the important information or ideas. |
| **2**   Reflects **partial** understanding of the text. Includes important information and ideas but neglects other key understandings. |
| **3**   Reflects **excellent** understanding of the text. Includes almost all important information and main ideas. |

| **Key Understandings** | **Prompts** | **Score** |
| --- | --- | --- |
| **Within the Text**<br><br>There are many different kinds of whales.<br><br>Lists 4–5 facts about whales, such as: whales are the biggest animals; there are different kinds and sizes of whales; whales live in the water; whales breathe air; a baby whale is called a calf; whales make different sounds to communicate with each other; you can see whales at a sea park or in the sea.<br><br>Describes a graphic and interprets it.<br><br>*Note any additional understandings:* | What were some of the important facts about whales that were in this book?<br><br>What are other facts that you learned?<br><br>*Text Feature Probe*<br><br>Look at the photograph and drawing on pages 2 and 3. What did you learn from these pages? | 0   1   2   3 |
| **Beyond the Text**<br><br>Whales are like people and land animals because they breathe air.<br><br>Whales make sounds to communicate with each other.<br><br>I learned that (2–3 kinds of information new to the reader).<br><br>*Note any additional understandings:* | How are whales like people and how are they different?<br><br>Why do whales make sounds?<br><br>What did you learn that was new information to you? | 0   1   2   3 |

*Continued on next page.*

Recording Forms

## Part Two: Comprehension Conversation *continued*

| Key Understandings | Prompts | Score |
|---|---|---|
| **About the Text**<br><br>The writer tells information in the pictures, in the paragraphs (or book), and in the charts.<br><br>The writing in this book is interesting because (gives any plausible reason).<br><br>The writer showed pictures of horses, elephants, and whales to compare the size. And, the writer said the whale is the biggest animal in the world.<br><br>*Note any additional understandings:* | Why do you think the writer included photographs and drawings in the book? Can you give me an example?<br><br>What did the writer do to make whales interesting to read about?<br><br>Some whales are really big. What did the writer of this book do to help us know just how big they are? | 0  1  2  3 |

**Guide to Total Score**

9–10 **Excellent** Comprehension

7–8 **Satisfactory** Comprehension

5–6 **Limited** Comprehension

0–4 **Unsatisfactory** Comprehension

Subtotal Score: _____ /9

Add 1 for any additional understandings: _____ /1

Total Score: _____ /10

---

## Part Three: Writing About Reading *(optional)*

Read the writing/drawing prompt on the next page to the student. Specify the amount of time for the student to complete the task. (See *Assessment Guide* for more information.)

**Writing About Reading Scoring Key**

0 Reflects **no** understanding of the text.

1 Reflects **very limited** understanding of the text.

2 Reflects **partial** understanding of the text.

3 Reflects **excellent** understanding of the text.

Student _____    Date _____

# Write about five interesting things you learned about whales. You can draw a picture to go with your writing.

Student _____    Grade _____    Date _____

Teacher _____    School _____

## Recording Form
### Part One: Oral Reading

Place the book in front of the student. Read the title and introduction.

*Introduction*:    A girl named Hanna is tired of her younger brother Nathan so she trades him for her friend Jerry's little brother William for the day. Read to find out what happened.

Sources of Information Used

| Page | Start Time ____ min. ____ sec.       *The Thing About Nathan* Level M, RW: 266 | E | SC | E | | | SC | | |
|---|---|---|---|---|---|---|---|---|---|
| | | | | M | S | V | M | S | V |
| 2 | "My little brother drives me crazy," said Hanna. "He is so messy! Nathan doesn't eat food. He wears it. And you wouldn't believe his room!" Hanna rolled her eyes. "It looks like a herd of cattle lives there." | | | | | | | | |
| 3 | "My brother is a neat freak," said Jerry. "William puts all his stuff away on a shelf in his room, with everything in perfect order, like the books in the library. And you'd better not touch anything." | | | | | | | | |
| | **Subtotal** | | | | | | | | |

**Part One: Oral Reading** *continued*

Sources of Information Used

| Page | Text | E | SC | E | | | SC | | |
|---|---|---|---|---|---|---|---|---|---|
| | | | | M | S | V | M | S | V |
| 4 | "I'd trade my messy brother for your neat one any day," said Hanna. "This Saturday, my parents are building a rock garden in the backyard. I'm supposed to keep Nathan busy. I know I'll go nuts." "Can Nathan swim?" Jerry asked. "He swims like a fish," said Hanna. "He could come with us on Saturday," Jerry suggested. "My family is going to the city pool. William doesn't really enjoy swimming. He'd rather stay home and work on his models." | | | | | | | | |
| 5 | "If you take Nathan swimming," said Hanna, "I'll ask my mom if William can | | | | | | | | |
| | **Subtotal** | | | | | | | | |

## Part One: Oral Reading *continued*

Sources of Information Used

| Page | Text | E | SC | E | | | SC | | |
|------|------|---|----|---|---|---|----|---|---|
| | | | | M | S | V | M | S | V |
| **5** *cont.* | come to our house. He can work on his<br><br>models or do whatever he wants."<br><br>"It's a deal!" shouted Jerry. | | | | | | | | |
| **6** | Saturday morning, Jerry's parents picked<br><br>up Nathan and dropped off William. Nathan<br><br>ran off with just his swimsuit and flip-flops.<br><br>William brought a backpack bursting<br><br>with stuff.<br><br>He brought a toothbrush and<br><br>toothpaste. "I always brush after I eat," he<br><br>said. He brought a clean shirt. "I might<br><br>spill something on this one." And he | | | | | | | | |
| | **Subtotal** | | | | | | | | |

**Part One: Oral Reading** *continued*

Sources of Information Used

| Page | Text | E | SC | E | | | SC | | |
|------|------|---|----|---|---|---|----|---|---|
| | | | | M | S | V | M | S | V |
| **6** *cont.* | brought two model kits and two videos. <br><br> "We have videos you can watch," <br><br> said Hanna. <br><br> "I like my own, thanks," said William. | | | | | | | | |
| | **Subtotal** | | | | | | | | |
| | **End Time** ____ min. ____ sec.    **Total** | | | | | | | | |

Have the student finish reading the book silently.

| Accuracy Rate | Errors | 15 or more | 12–14 | 10–11 | 7–9 | 5–6 | 1–4 |
|---|---|---|---|---|---|---|---|
| | % | Below 95% | 95% | 96% | 97% | 98% | 99% |

**Self-Correction Ratio**

(E + SC) ÷ SC = 1: ____

**Fluency Score**      0   1   2   3

**Fluency Scoring Key**

**0**   Reads primarily word-by-word with occasional but infrequent or inappropriate phrasing; no smooth or expressive interpretation, irregular pausing, and no attention to author's meaning or punctuation; no stress or inappropriate stress, and slow rate.

**1**   Reads primarily in two-word phrases with some three- and four-word groups and some word-by-word reading; almost no smooth, expressive interpretation or pausing guided by author's meaning and punctuation; almost no stress or inappropriate stress, with slow rate most of the time.

**2**   Reads primarily in three- or four-word phrase groups; some smooth, expressive interpretation and pausing guided by author's meaning and punctuation; mostly appropriate stress and rate with some slowdowns.

**3**   Reads primarily in larger, meaningful phrases or word groups; mostly smooth, expressive interpretation and pausing guided by author's meaning and punctuation; appropriate stress and rate with only a few slowdowns.

**Reading Rate**
*(Optional)*

End Time      ____ min. ____ sec.
Start Time    ____ min. ____ sec.
Total Time    ____ min. ____ sec.
Total Seconds    _____

(RW × 60) ÷ Total Seconds = Words Per Minute (WPM)
15,960 ÷ _____ = _____ WPM

Recording Forms

## Part Two: Comprehension Conversation

Have a conversation with the student, noting the key understandings the student expresses. Use prompts as needed to stimulate discussion of understandings the student does not express. Score for evidence of all understandings expressed—with or without a prompt. Circle the number in the score column that reflects the level of understanding demonstrated.

*Teacher*: Talk about what happened in this story.

| Key Understandings | Prompts | Score |
|---|---|---|
| **Within the Text**<br><br>Recounts most of the events of the story, such as: Hanna wanted to get rid of her little brother Nathan; she decided to trade him for her friend Jerry's little brother William for the day; she had a problem because William was different from Nathan (gives an example: fussy, picky eater, no fun); Hanna gave Nathan a big hug when he came back.<br><br>*Note any additional understandings:* | What was the problem in this story?<br><br>How did Hanna try to solve the problem?<br><br>What happened after they traded brothers?<br><br>How did the story end? | 0  1  2  3 |
| **Beyond the Text**<br><br>Hanna's little brother drove her crazy because (gives a plausible reason).<br><br>Hanna started to get annoyed with William.<br><br>Hanna began to realize that she liked Nathan compared to William.<br><br>Hanna was surprised to find that she missed Nathan after all.<br><br>*Note any additional understandings:* | How did Hanna feel about Nathan at the beginning of the story?<br><br>How did Hanna feel about William?<br><br>How did Hanna's feelings toward Nathan change and why?<br><br>What was surprising to her after they traded brothers? | 0  1  2  3 |

*Continued on next page.*

Recording Forms

## Part Two: Comprehension Conversation *continued*

| Key Understandings | Prompts | Score |
|---|---|---|
| **About the Text**<br><br>Hanna started to change her mind about Nathan after being with William.<br><br>You could tell what Nathan was like by what Hanna was saying and thinking about him and William.<br><br>This story had a lesson (seeing someone else's brother helped her realize she really liked her own brother or that her brother wasn't so bad after all).<br><br>*Note any additional understandings:* | When did Hanna start to change her mind about Nathan?<br><br>How did the writer show what Nathan was like even though he wasn't in the story most of the time?<br><br>The writer was showing how Hanna learned a lesson. What was the important lesson Hanna learned? | 0   1   2   3 |

**Guide to Total Score**

9–10 **Excellent** Comprehension

7–8 **Satisfactory** Comprehension

5–6 **Limited** Comprehension

0–4 **Unsatisfactory** Comprehension

Subtotal Score: _____ /9

Add 1 for any additional understandings: _____ /1

Total Score: _____ /10

---

## Part Three: Writing About Reading *(optional)*

Read the writing/drawing prompt on the next page to the student. Specify the amount of time for the student to complete the task. (See *Assessment Guide* for more information.)

**Writing About Reading Scoring Key**

**0** Reflects **no** understanding of the text.

**1** Reflects **very limited** understanding of the text.

**2** Reflects **partial** understanding of the text.

**3** Reflects **excellent** understanding of the text.

Student _____     Date _____

Think about Hanna's point of view. Write about three of William's behaviors that are annoying. Compare them to Nathan's. You can draw a picture to go with your writing.

Student _____  Grade _____  Date _____

Teacher _____  School _____

## Recording Form

### Part One: Oral Reading

Place the book in front of the student. Read the title and introduction.

*Introduction*:  In this book, you will learn how a monarch butterfly changes from an egg to a caterpillar. Read to find out how it turns its skin into a chrysalis and comes out as a butterfly.

|  |  |  | | | E | | | SC | | |
|---|---|---|---|---|---|---|---|---|---|---|
| **Page** | **Start Time ____ min. ____ sec.** *The Life of a Monarch Butterfly* Level M, RW: 223 | **E** | **SC** | **M** | **S** | **V** | **M** | **S** | **V** | |

*Sources of Information Used*

| Page | | E | SC | E-M | E-S | E-V | SC-M | SC-S | SC-V |
|---|---|---|---|---|---|---|---|---|---|
| 2 | Do you see the speck on this leaf? It's a tiny egg! <br><br> A monarch butterfly laid <br><br> the egg. Someday, after many <br><br> changes have taken place, the <br><br> egg will become a beautiful <br><br> butterfly. | | | | | | | | |
| 3 | [Egg] <br><br> Every butterfly starts out as <br><br> an egg. The female butterfly <br><br> looks for a good place to lay | | | | | | | | |
| | **Subtotal** | | | | | | | | |

Recording Forms

## Part One: Oral Reading *continued*

Sources of Information Used

| Page | Text | E | SC | E | | | SC | | |
|---|---|---|---|---|---|---|---|---|---|
| | | | | M | S | V | M | S | V |
| **3** *cont.* | her eggs. Monarch butterflies lay their eggs on milkweed plants. | | | | | | | | |
| **4** | [Caterpillar]<br><br>The eggs hatch after a few days. You might be expecting a tiny butterfly. But instead, a tiny caterpillar crawls out of each egg. A newborn caterpillar is so small you can hardly see it. But it will not stay small very long.<br><br>As soon as the caterpillar hatches, it starts to eat. | | | | | | | | |
| | **Subtotal** | | | | | | | | |

© 2008 by Irene C. Fountas and Gay Su Pinnell. Portsmouth, NH: Heinemann. This page may be photocopied.

**Part One: Oral Reading** *continued*

Sources of Information Used

| Page | Text | E | SC | E | | | SC | | |
|------|------|---|----|---|---|---|----|---|---|
| | | | | M | S | V | M | S | V |
| 5 | First the newborn caterpillar eats its own eggshell. Then it starts to eat the milkweed plant. It crunches and munches like an eating machine! The caterpillar eats and eats and eats. The more it eats, the larger it grows. The caterpillar's skin starts to get tight, like a pair of pants that are too small. | | | | | | | | |
| | **Subtotal** | | | | | | | | |

**Part One: Oral Reading** *continued*

Sources of Information Used

| Page | Text | E | SC | E | | | SC | | |
|------|------|---|----|---|---|---|----|---|---|
| | | | | M | S | V | M | S | V |
| 6 | Soon the caterpillar's old skin splits open! But the caterpillar has been growing a new, larger skin underneath the old skin. When the old skin breaks, the caterpillar crawls right out of it. This happens again and again. Because it grows so fast, the caterpillar will change its skin five times before it is fully grown. | | | | | | | | |
| | **Subtotal** | | | | | | | | |
| | **Total** | | | | | | | | |

**End Time** _____ min. _____ sec.

Have the student finish reading the book silently.

Recording Forms

| **Accuracy Rate** | **Errors** | **13 or more** | **11–12** | **8–10** | **6–7** | **4–5** | **1–3** |
|---|---|---|---|---|---|---|---|
| | **%** | Below 95% | 95% | 96% | 97% | 98% | 99% |

**Self-Correction Ratio**

(E + SC) ÷ SC = 1: \_\_\_\_

**Fluency Score**

0    1    2    3

**Fluency Scoring Key**

**0**  Reads primarily word-by-word with occasional but infrequent or inappropriate phrasing; no smooth or expressive interpretation, irregular pausing, and no attention to author's meaning or punctuation; no stress or inappropriate stress, and slow rate.

**1**  Reads primarily in two-word phrases with some three- and four-word groups and some word-by-word reading; almost no smooth, expressive interpretation or pausing guided by author's meaning and punctuation; almost no stress or inappropriate stress, with slow rate most of the time.

**2**  Reads primarily in three- or four-word phrase groups; some smooth, expressive interpretation and pausing guided by author's meaning and punctuation; mostly appropriate stress and rate with some slowdowns.

**3**  Reads primarily in larger, meaningful phrases or word groups; mostly smooth, expressive interpretation and pausing guided by author's meaning and punctuation; appropriate stress and rate with only a few slowdowns.

**Reading Rate**
*(Optional)*

End Time        \_\_\_\_ min. \_\_\_\_ sec.

Start Time      \_\_\_\_ min. \_\_\_\_ sec.

Total Time      \_\_\_\_ min. \_\_\_\_ sec.

Total Seconds   _____

(RW × 60) ÷ Total Seconds = Words Per Minute (WPM)

13,380 ÷ _____ = _____ WPM

## Part Two: Comprehension Conversation

Have a conversation with the student, noting the key understandings the student expresses. Use prompts as needed to stimulate discussion of understandings the student does not express. Score for evidence of all understandings expressed—with or without a prompt. Circle the number in the score column that reflects the level of understanding demonstrated.

*Teacher:*   Talk about what you learned in this book.

| Comprehension Scoring Key | |
|---|---|
| **0** | Reflects **no** understanding of the text. Either does not respond or talks off the topic. |
| **1** | Reflects **very limited** understanding of the text. Mentions a few facts or ideas but does not express the important information or ideas. |
| **2** | Reflects **partial** understanding of the text. Includes important information and ideas but neglects other key understandings. |
| **3** | Reflects **excellent** understanding of the text. Includes almost all important information and main ideas. |

| Key Understandings | Prompts | Score |
|---|---|---|
| **Within the Text**<br><br>Describes important parts of the butterfly's life cycle: the butterfly lays an egg; the egg hatches; a caterpillar crawls out; the caterpillar eats and eats; the caterpillar's skin gets tight and splits five times; the caterpillar hangs upside down; the caterpillar has a chrysalis; the caterpillar changes to a butterfly; the butterfly comes out; the butterfly lays eggs.<br><br>*Note any additional understandings:* | Tell how an egg becomes a butterfly. What happens first? Then what happens? Then what? | 0   1   2   3 |
| **Beyond the Text**<br><br>The egg becomes a butterfly, then the butterfly lays an egg, then the egg becomes a butterfly again.<br><br>*Note any additional understandings:* | How does the life cycle of a monarch butterfly keep repeating? | 0   1   2   3 |

*Continued on next page.*

Recording Forms

## Part Two: Comprehension Conversation *continued*

| Key Understandings | Prompts | Score |
|---|---|---|
| **About the Text**<br><br>The writer described everything in the order it happens.<br><br><br>The writer gave information in lots of different ways, such as: headings to the sections; diagrams; photographs; captions for pictures.<br><br>*Note any additional understandings:* | The writer told the information in a special way to make it easy for you to understand how an egg turns into a butterfly. What did the writer do?<br><br>In addition to the main part of the book, what are some of the other ways the writer told information about the monarch butterfly? | 0  1  2  3 |

**Guide to Total Score**

9–10 **Excellent** Comprehension

7–8 **Satisfactory** Comprehension

5–6 **Limited** Comprehension

0–4 **Unsatisfactory** Comprehension

Subtotal Score: _____ /9

Add 1 for any additional understandings: _____ /1

Total Score: _____ /10

---

## Part Three: Writing About Reading *(optional)*

Read the writing/drawing prompt on the next page to the student. Specify the amount of time for the student to complete the task. (See *Assessment Guide* for more information.)

**Writing About Reading Scoring Key**

**0** Reflects **no** understanding of the text.

**1** Reflects **very limited** understanding of the text.

**2** Reflects **partial** understanding of the text.

**3** Reflects **excellent** understanding of the text.

Student _____ Date _____

Write about three interesting things you learned about the life of a monarch butterfly. You can draw a picture to go with your writing.

Student _____   Grade _____   Date _____

Teacher _____   School _____

## Recording Form

### Part One: Oral Reading

Place the book in front of the student. Read the title and introduction.

*Introduction*:   It was the first big snowstorm in Chicago. When Patrick Waite left school at the end of the day, the problems began. Read to find out what happened to Patrick and his family.

Sources of Information Used

| Page | Start Time ____ min. ____ sec.                     *The Big Snow* Level N, RW: 259 | E | SC | E | | | SC | | |
|---|---|---|---|---|---|---|---|---|---|
| | | | | M | S | V | M | S | V |
| 2 | With five minutes left in the school day, not a single student in room 314 was thinking about school. Outside, snow was falling, piling up like a thick blanket on the street. It was Chicago's first big storm of the year. From Patrick Waite's seat two rows from the window, it looked like six inches had already fallen. The snowflakes were huge and fluffy. Patrick felt dizzy watching them tumble from the sky. When the bell finally rang, he hurried out the door and down the sidewalk in ankle-deep snow. | | | | | | | | | |
| | **Subtotal** | | | | | | | | |

**Part One: Oral Reading** *continued*

Sources of Information Used

| Page | Text | E | SC | E | | | SC | | |
|------|------|---|----|---|---|---|----|---|---|
| | | | | M | S | V | M | S | V |
| 3 | "Looks like the number six bus is stuck!" Mr. Henry said. A stuck bus didn't matter to Patrick. His family's apartment was just five blocks from the school, and he always walked. Patrick grinned. Today, he could pretend he was hiking at the North Pole. | | | | | | | | |
| 4 | Patrick's good mood vanished after two blocks. His feet were soaked and his face felt frozen. As he waited to cross Western Avenue, a huge snowplow rolled past. It sprayed him with snow and slush. "Thanks a lot!" Patrick yelled. The driver smiled and waved. | | | | | | | | |
| | **Subtotal** | | | | | | | | |

**Part One: Oral Reading** *continued*

Sources of Information Used

| Page | Text | E | SC | E | | | SC | | |
|---|---|---|---|---|---|---|---|---|---|
| | | | | M | S | V | M | S | V |
| 6 | It seemed to take hours to walk home. Finally, Patrick stepped into the warm lobby of his apartment building. He got the mail and rode the elevator up to the tenth floor. As he opened the door, Patrick was surprised to find the apartment empty. Where was everyone? Dad and his brothers always beat him home. Patrick shook off his soggy coat and tried to ignore the uneasy feeling growing in his stomach. Maybe he was just hungry. | | | | | | | | |
| | **Subtotal** | | | | | | | | |
| | End Time ____ min. ____ sec.    **Total** | | | | | | | | |

Have the student finish reading the book silently.

Recording Forms

| Accuracy Rate | Errors | 15 or more | 12–14 | 10–11 | 7–9 | 4–6 | 1–3 |
|---|---|---|---|---|---|---|---|
| | % | Below 95% | 95% | 96% | 97% | 98% | 99% |

**Self-Correction Ratio**

(E + SC) ÷ SC = 1: _____

**Fluency Score**

0   1   2   3

**Fluency Scoring Key**

**0**   Reads primarily word-by-word with occasional but infrequent or inappropriate phrasing; no smooth or expressive interpretation, irregular pausing, and no attention to author's meaning or punctuation; no stress or inappropriate stress, and slow rate.

**1**   Reads primarily in two-word phrases with some three- and four-word groups and some word-by-word reading; almost no smooth, expressive interpretation or pausing guided by author's meaning and punctuation; almost no stress or inappropriate stress, with slow rate most of the time.

**2**   Reads primarily in three- or four-word phrase groups; some smooth, expressive interpretation and pausing guided by author's meaning and punctuation; mostly appropriate stress and rate with some slowdowns.

**3**   Reads primarily in larger, meaningful phrases or word groups; mostly smooth, expressive interpretation and pausing guided by author's meaning and punctuation; appropriate stress and rate with only a few slowdowns.

**Reading Rate**
*(Optional)*

End Time        _____ min. _____ sec.
Start Time      _____ min. _____ sec.
Total Time      _____ min. _____ sec.
Total Seconds   _____

(RW × 60) ÷ Total Seconds = Words Per Minute (WPM)

15,540 ÷ _____ = _____ WPM

## Part Two: Comprehension Conversation

Have a conversation with the student, noting the key understandings the student expresses. Use prompts as needed to stimulate discussion of understandings the student does not express. Score for evidence of all understandings expressed—with or without a prompt. Circle the number in the score column that reflects the level of understanding demonstrated.

*Teacher*:     Talk about what happened in this story.

<table>
<tr><td colspan="2">

**Comprehension Scoring Key**

**0**   Reflects **no** understanding of the text. Either does not respond or talks off the topic.

**1**   Reflects **very limited** understanding of the text. Mentions a few facts or ideas but does not express the important information or ideas.

**2**   Reflects **partial** understanding of the text. Includes important information and ideas but neglects other key understandings.

**3**   Reflects **excellent** understanding of the text. Includes almost all important information and main ideas.

</td></tr>
</table>

| Key Understandings | Prompts | Score |
|---|---|---|
| **Within the Text**<br><br>There was a huge snowstorm in Chicago and it was causing a lot of problems.<br><br>Recounts important episodes in the sequence of events, such as: Snow is falling; Patrick struggles home and finds no one there; the lights go off; Patrick and his family solve a lot of problems; Dad is still not home; everyone finally gets home.<br><br>In the end, they were okay. They were all home (or his dad was home).<br><br>*Note any additional understandings:* | What was the big problem at the beginning of the story?<br><br>What were some of the problems that Patrick had?<br><br>How did Patrick solve the problems?<br><br>How did the story end? | 0  1  2  3 |
| **Beyond the Text**<br><br>This reminds me of when our lights went out (or provides a similar example).<br><br>Patrick started to get scared when he got home and was alone.<br><br>His dad was a really nice person because he was always helping people.<br><br>Patrick did a good job of (gives a plausible answer). He didn't complain but just did what he needed to do.<br><br>*Note any additional understandings:* | Have you ever had an experience like this?<br><br>How did Patrick feel when he got home alone?<br><br>What kind of person do you think Patrick's dad was?<br><br>What kind of person do you think Patrick was? | 0  1  2  3 |

*Continued on next page.*

## Part Two: Comprehension Conversation *continued*

| Key Understandings | Prompts | Score |
|---|---|---|
| **About the Text**<br><br>The writer told what Patrick was thinking to show how worried he was about the dangerous snowstorm.<br><br>The writer showed what kind of person Patrick was by telling everything he did.<br><br>*Note any additional understandings:* | How did the writer help you know this was a kind of dangerous situation?<br><br>How did the writer show you what kind of person Patrick was? | 0   1   2   3 |

**Guide to Total Score**

9–10 **Excellent** Comprehension

7–8 **Satisfactory** Comprehension

5–6 **Limited** Comprehension

0–4 **Unsatisfactory** Comprehension

Subtotal Score: _____ /9

Add 1 for any additional understandings: _____ /1

Total Score: _____ /10

## Part Three: Writing About Reading *(optional)*

Read the writing/drawing prompt on the next page to the student. Specify the amount of time for the student to complete the task. (See *Assessment Guide* for more information.)

**Writing About Reading Scoring Key**

0 Reflects **no** understanding of the text.

1 Reflects **very limited** understanding of the text.

2 Reflects **partial** understanding of the text.

3 Reflects **excellent** understanding of the text.

Recording Forms

Student _____     Date _____

Write about Patrick's feelings and how they changed from the
beginning to the middle and at the end of the story. You can draw
a picture to go with your writing.

Student _____     Grade _____     Date _____

Teacher _____     School _____

# Recording Form

## Part One: Oral Reading

Place the book in front of the student. Read the title and introduction.

*Introduction*:   In this book, you will learn about how caves are formed. You will read about the formations in caves—stalactites that hang from the ceiling and stalagmites that come up from the floor. Read to learn all about caves.

Sources of Information Used

| Page | Start Time ____ min. ____ sec. | *Exploring Caves* Level N, RW: 272 | E | SC | E | | | SC | | |
|---|---|---|---|---|---|---|---|---|---|---|
| | | | | | M | S | V | M | S | V |
| 2 | [Caves and Cavers]<br><br>Caves are dark, hidden worlds<br><br>that some people like to explore.<br><br>These people are called *cavers*.<br><br>Some big caves, called *caverns*,<br><br>have rooms that connect, just like<br><br>a house. Cavers have fun crawling,<br><br>climbing, and sliding through rocky<br><br>spaces—some tiny, some huge—to<br><br>learn about these interesting places. | | | | | | | | | |
| | | **Subtotal** | | | | | | | | |

**Part One: Oral Reading** *continued*

Sources of Information Used

| Page | Text | E | SC | E | | | SC | | |
|------|------|---|----|---|---|---|----|---|---|
| | | | | M | S | V | M | S | V |
| 4 | [How Are Caves Formed?]<br><br>Scientists have different ideas about how caves are formed. Most think caves are created by water.<br><br>When rain falls, it mixes with an invisible gas in the air. When the water reaches the ground, it seeps into the earth. | | | | | | | | |
| 5 | The water continues going deeper into the earth until it touches rock. Very slowly, the water eats away at the rock and causes tiny cracks to develop. The cracks in the rock grow wider with time. Then the water flows out and leaves behind a cave. | | | | | | | | |
| | **Subtotal** | | | | | | | | |

**Part One: Oral Reading** *continued*

Sources of Information Used

| Page | Text | E | SC | E | | | SC | | |
|------|------|---|----|---|---|---|----|---|---|
| | | | | M | S | V | M | S | V |
| 6 | [Safety First] | | | | | | | | |
| | Guides work at many cave sites. | | | | | | | | |
| | These experts can lead people through the | | | | | | | | |
| | twisting tunnels and paths inside caves | | | | | | | | |
| | without getting lost. | | | | | | | | |
| | Cavers love adventure, but they have | | | | | | | | |
| | to be smart and careful. One rule they | | | | | | | | |
| | follow is never to explore alone. There | | | | | | | | |
| | must be at least three people in a group. | | | | | | | | |
| | That way, if there's an accident, someone | | | | | | | | |
| | can go get help. | | | | | | | | |
| | **Subtotal** | | | | | | | | |

Recording Forms

**Part One: Oral Reading** *continued*

Sources of Information Used

| Page | Text | E | SC | E | | | SC | | |
|------|------|---|----|---|---|---|----|---|---|
| | | | | M | S | V | M | S | V |
| 7 | Cavers follow another rule—be prepared! It can get very cold inside a cave, so cavers wear warm clothing. They also wear helmets to protect their heads from falling rocks. Sturdy hiking boots help them walk along bumpy or slippery paths. | | | | | | | | |
| 8 | It's very dark inside a cave, but instead of carrying flashlights, many cavers wear helmets with lights attached to them. That way their hands are free to hold on as they climb on rocks. | | | | | | | | |
| | **Subtotal** | | | | | | | | |
| | **End Time** ____ min. ____ sec.  **Total** | | | | | | | | |

Have the student finish reading the book silently.

© 2008 by Irene C. Fountas and Gay Su Pinnell. Portsmouth, NH: Heinemann. This page may be photocopied.

Recording Forms

| Accuracy Rate | Errors | 15 or more | 13–14 | 10–12 | 7–9 | 5–6 | 1–4 |
|---|---|---|---|---|---|---|---|
| % | | Below 95% | 95% | 96% | 97% | 98% | 99% |

**Self-Correction Ratio**

(E + SC) ÷ SC = 1: ____

**Fluency Score**

0   1   2   3

**Fluency Scoring Key**

**0**   Reads primarily word-by-word with occasional but infrequent or inappropriate phrasing; no smooth or expressive interpretation, irregular pausing, and no attention to author's meaning or punctuation; no stress or inappropriate stress, and slow rate.

**1**   Reads primarily in two-word phrases with some three- and four-word groups and some word-by-word reading; almost no smooth, expressive interpretation or pausing guided by author's meaning and punctuation; almost no stress or inappropriate stress, with slow rate most of the time.

**2**   Reads primarily in three- or four-word phrase groups; some smooth, expressive interpretation and pausing guided by author's meaning and punctuation; mostly appropriate stress and rate with some slowdowns.

**3**   Reads primarily in larger, meaningful phrases or word groups; mostly smooth, expressive interpretation and pausing guided by author's meaning and punctuation; appropriate stress and rate with only a few slowdowns.

**Reading Rate** *(Optional)*

End Time        ____ min. ____ sec.

Start Time      ____ min. ____ sec.

Total Time      ____ min. ____ sec.

Total Seconds   _____

(RW × 60) ÷ Total Seconds = Words Per Minute (WPM)

16,320 ÷ _____ = _____ WPM

## Part Two: Comprehension Conversation

Have a conversation with the student, noting the key understandings the student expresses. Use prompts as needed to stimulate discussion of understandings the student does not express. Score for evidence of all understandings expressed—with or without a prompt. Circle the number in the score column that reflects the level of understanding demonstrated.

*Teacher*:   Talk about what you learned in this book.

| Comprehension Scoring Key |
|---|
| **0**  Reflects **no** understanding of the text. Either does not respond or talks off the topic. |
| **1**  Reflects **very limited** understanding of the text. Mentions a few facts or ideas but does not express the important information or ideas. |
| **2**  Reflects **partial** understanding of the text. Includes important information and ideas but neglects other key understandings. |
| **3**  Reflects **excellent** understanding of the text. Includes almost all important information and main ideas. |

| Key Understandings | Prompts | Score |
|---|---|---|
| **Within the Text**<br><br>Caves are spaces under the ground.<br><br>Reports 3–4 interesting facts about caves, such as: people who like to explore caves are cavers; caves have rooms; water eats away at the rock to make a cave; three people need to go together in a cave; cavers wear warm clothes, helmets with lights, and hiking boots; animals live in caves; water drips form stalactites and stalagmites.<br><br>*Note any additional understandings:* | What is a cave?<br><br>What did you learn about caves?<br><br>What else? | 0   1   2   3 |
| **Beyond the Text**<br><br>Caves are very important, and we need to take care of them.<br><br>Recounts one major idea from the text, such as: It takes a long time to make a cave; caves are home to many animals, so we need to take care of them; we can learn a lot about Earth from caves.<br><br>I would like to explore a cave because (gives a plausible reason).<br><br>*Note any additional understandings:* | What was the most important idea in this book?<br><br>What did you learn about why caves are important to us?<br><br>I might (or might not) like to explore a cave, would you? Why (not)? | 0   1   2   3 |

*Continued on next page.*

## Part Two: Comprehension Conversation *continued*

| Key Understandings | Prompts | Score |
|---|---|---|
| **About the Text**<br><br>The writer put information in the book that she thought readers would not know and would find interesting (gives examples).<br><br>The author read a lot about caves to learn about them and so she could write accurately about them. The facts must be right in this book because (gives author's credentials, references, other).<br><br>There are different kinds of information in different places in the book. The sections (or headings, titles, table of contents) tell you where to look.<br><br>The writer wants you to think that caves are very interesting and make you want to visit one or read more about them.<br><br>*Note any additional understandings:* | How do you think the writer decided what information to put in the book?<br><br>Do you think the information in this book is accurate? Why (not)?<br><br><br>How does the writer help you find the different kinds of information in this book?<br><br><br>What do you think the author wants you to think about caves? What do you think she might want you to do after you read this book? | 0    1    2    3 |

**Guide to Total Score**

9–10 **Excellent** Comprehension

7–8 **Satisfactory** Comprehension

5–6 **Limited** Comprehension

0–4 **Unsatisfactory** Comprehension

Subtotal Score: _____ /9

Add 1 for any additional understandings: _____ /1

Total Score: _____ /10

---

## Part Three: Writing About Reading *(optional)*

Read the writing/drawing prompt on the next page to the student. Specify the amount of time for the student to complete the task. (See *Assessment Guide* for more information.)

**Writing About Reading Scoring Key**

0 Reflects **no** understanding of the text.

1 Reflects **very limited** understanding of the text.

2 Reflects **partial** understanding of the text.

3 Reflects **excellent** understanding of the text.

Recording Forms

Student _____     Date _____

Write about five interesting things you learned about caves. You can draw a picture to go with your writing.

# Summary Forms

The following section includes a variety of useful forms for summarizing the information from your benchmark assessment conferences. The summary forms will help you analyze an individual student's performance or the performance of your whole class. You will also find forms for constructing a graph of student progress over time. You can photocopy these forms or print them from the *Forms CD-ROM*.

| Benchmark Independent Level* | _____ |
| Benchmark Instructional Level** | _____ |
| Recommended Placement Level | _____ |

Student _____  Grade _____  Date _____

Teacher _____  School _____

## Assessment Summary Form

List the titles read by the student from lowest to highest level.

| Title | System 1 or 2 | Fiction/ Nonfiction | Level | Accuracy | Comprehension | Independent * (check one) | Instructional ** (check one) | Self-Correction | Fluency Levels C–Z | Rate Levels J–Z (optional) | Writing About Reading (optional) |
|---|---|---|---|---|---|---|---|---|---|---|---|
| | | | | | | | | | | | |
| | | | | | | | | | | | |
| | | | | | | | | | | | |
| | | | | | | | | | | | |
| | | | | | | | | | | | |

**\*Independent Level:**

**Levels A–K:** Highest level read with 95–100% accuracy and excellent or satisfactory comprehension.

**Levels L–Z:** Highest level read with 98–100% accuracy and excellent or satisfactory comprehension.

**\*\*Instructional Level**

**Levels A–K:** Highest level read with 90–94% accuracy and excellent or satisfactory comprehension or 95–100% accuracy and limited comprehension.

**Levels L–Z:** Highest level read with 95–97% accuracy and excellent or satisfactory comprehension or 98–100% accuracy and limited comprehension.

**Comprehension**

| Levels A–K | | Levels L–Z | |
|---|---|---|---|
| 6–7 | Excellent | 9–10 | Excellent |
| 5 | Satisfactory | 7–8 | Satisfactory |
| 4 | Limited | 5–6 | Limited |
| 0–3 | Unsatisfactory | 0–4 | Unsatisfactory |

**Additional Comments:**

**Instructional Implications:**

Student _____  Grade _____  Year _____

Teacher _____  School _____

## Bi-Annual Assessment Summary

| | Date _____ | Date _____ |
|---|---|---|
| **Independent Level** | Level _____ | Level _____ |
| Accuracy | _____ % | _____ % |
| Comprehension | _____ / _____ | _____ / _____ |
| Self-Correction | _____ | _____ |
| Fluency | 0   1   2   3 | 0   1   2   3 |
| Rate *(optional)* | _____ WPM | _____ WPM |
| Writing About Reading *(optional)* | 0   1   2   3 | 0   1   2   3 |
| **Instructional Level** | Level _____ | Level _____ |
| Accuracy | _____ % | _____ % |
| Comprehension | _____ / _____ | _____ / _____ |
| Self-Correction | _____ | _____ |
| Fluency | 0   1   2   3 | 0   1   2   3 |
| Rate *(optional)* | _____ WPM | _____ WPM |
| Writing About Reading *(optional)* | 0   1   2   3 | 0   1   2   3 |

**Additional Comments**

Student _____   Grade _____   Year _____

Teacher _____   School _____

## Tri-Annual Assessment Summary

| | Date _____ | Date _____ | Date _____ |
|---|---|---|---|
| **Independent Level** | Level _____ | Level _____ | Level _____ |
| Accuracy | _____ % | _____ % | _____ % |
| Comprehension | _____ / _____ | _____ / _____ | _____ / _____ |
| Self-Correction | _____ | _____ | _____ |
| Fluency | 0  1  2  3 | 0  1  2  3 | 0  1  2  3 |
| Rate *(optional)* | _____ WPM | _____ WPM | _____ WPM |
| Writing About Reading *(optional)* | 0  1  2  3 | 0  1  2  3 | 0  1  2  3 |
| **Instructional Level** | Level _____ | Level _____ | Level _____ |
| Accuracy | _____ % | _____ % | _____ % |
| Comprehension | _____ / _____ | _____ / _____ | _____ / _____ |
| Self-Correction | _____ | _____ | _____ |
| Fluency | 0  1  2  3 | 0  1  2  3 | 0  1  2  3 |
| Rate *(optional)* | _____ WPM | _____ WPM | _____ WPM |
| Writing About Reading *(optional)* | 0  1  2  3 | 0  1  2  3 | 0  1  2  3 |

**Additional Comments**

Summary Forms

Student _____ Grade _____ Year _____

Teacher _____ School _____

## Quarterly Assessment Summary

| | Date _____ | Date _____ | Date _____ | Date _____ |
|---|---|---|---|---|
| **Independent Level** | Level _____ | Level _____ | Level _____ | Level _____ |
| Accuracy | _____ % | _____ % | _____ % | _____ % |
| Comprehension | _____ / _____ | _____ / _____ | _____ / _____ | _____ / _____ |
| Self-Correction | _____ | _____ | _____ | _____ |
| Fluency | 0  1  2  3 | 0  1  2  3 | 0  1  2  3 | 0  1  2  3 |
| Rate *(optional)* | _____ WPM | _____ WPM | _____ WPM | _____ WPM |
| Writing About Reading *(optional)* | 0  1  2  3 | 0  1  2  3 | 0  1  2  3 | 0  1  2  3 |
| **Instructional Level** | Level _____ | Level _____ | Level _____ | Level _____ |
| Accuracy | _____ % | _____ % | _____ % | _____ % |
| Comprehension | _____ / _____ | _____ / _____ | _____ / _____ | _____ / _____ |
| Self-Correction | _____ | _____ | _____ | _____ |
| Fluency | 0  1  2  3 | 0  1  2  3 | 0  1  2  3 | 0  1  2  3 |
| Rate *(optional)* | _____ WPM | _____ WPM | _____ WPM | _____ WPM |
| Writing About Reading *(optional)* | 0  1  2  3 | 0  1  2  3 | 0  1  2  3 | 0  1  2  3 |

**Additional Comments**

Summary Forms

Teacher _____     Grade _____     Year _____

School _____

Date _____

## Class Record Form

| Student Name | Benchmark Independent Level | Benchmark Instructional Level | Accur. | Comp. | Fluency | Benchmark Placement Level | Notes |
|---|---|---|---|---|---|---|---|
| 1. | | | | | | | |
| 2. | | | | | | | |
| 3. | | | | | | | |
| 4. | | | | | | | |
| 5. | | | | | | | |
| 6. | | | | | | | |
| 7. | | | | | | | |
| 8. | | | | | | | |
| 9. | | | | | | | |
| 10. | | | | | | | |
| 11. | | | | | | | |
| 12. | | | | | | | |
| 13. | | | | | | | |
| 14. | | | | | | | |
| 15. | | | | | | | |
| 16. | | | | | | | |
| 17. | | | | | | | |
| 18. | | | | | | | |
| 19. | | | | | | | |
| 20. | | | | | | | |
| 21. | | | | | | | |
| 22. | | | | | | | |
| 23. | | | | | | | |
| 24. | | | | | | | |
| 25. | | | | | | | |
| 26. | | | | | | | |
| 27. | | | | | | | |
| 28. | | | | | | | |
| 29. | | | | | | | |
| 30. | | | | | | | |

© 2008 by Irene C. Fountas and Gay Su Pinnell. Portsmouth, NH: Heinemann. This page may be photocopied.

Summary Forms

Student _____ Grade _____

Teacher _____ School _____

## Annual Record of Reading Progress

Record the title and accuracy rate. Draw a circle to indicate text level.

● = below 90% (Levels A–K) or below 95% (Levels L–Z)   ○ = 90% or above (Levels A–K) or 95% or above (Levels L–Z)

# Longitudinal Record of Reading Progress

Student _____  School _____

Record the date and draw a circle in the box to indicate student's level. Check one: _____ Benchmark Independent Level     _____ Benchmark Instructional Level

| | Level Benchmark Title | | | | | K | | 1 | | 2 | | 3 | | 4 | | 5 | | 6 | | 7 | | 8 | |
|---|---|---|---|---|---|---|---|---|---|---|---|---|---|---|---|---|---|---|---|---|---|---|---|
| System 2 | Z ☐ Train at the Top | | | | | | | | | | | | | | | | | | | | | | |
| | ☐ Surviving the Blitz | | | | | | | | | | | | | | | | | | | | | | |
| | Y ☐ Int'l Space Station | | | | | | | | | | | | | | | | | | | | | | |
| | ☐ Saying Goodbye | | | | | | | | | | | | | | | | | | | | | | |
| | X ☐ The Internet | | | | | | | | | | | | | | | | | | | | | | |
| | ☐ A Weighty Decision | | | | | | | | | | | | | | | | | | | | | | |
| | W ☐ Coretta Scott King | | | | | | | | | | | | | | | | | | | | | | |
| | ☐ Summer Vacation | | | | | | | | | | | | | | | | | | | | | | |
| | V ☐ Tsunamis | | | | | | | | | | | | | | | | | | | | | | |
| | ☐ A Call for Change | | | | | | | | | | | | | | | | | | | | | | |
| | U ☐ Earthquakes | | | | | | | | | | | | | | | | | | | | | | |
| | ☐ Canyon Mystery | | | | | | | | | | | | | | | | | | | | | | |
| | T ☐ Wolves Howl | | | | | | | | | | | | | | | | | | | | | | |
| | ☐ "Get a Horse!" | | | | | | | | | | | | | | | | | | | | | | |
| | S ☐ Animal Adaptations | | | | | | | | | | | | | | | | | | | | | | |
| | ☐ Could Be Worse | | | | | | | | | | | | | | | | | | | | | | |
| | R ☐ Fishing Smarts | | | | | | | | | | | | | | | | | | | | | | |
| | ☐ The Election | | | | | | | | | | | | | | | | | | | | | | |
| | Q ☐ Polar Bear | | | | | | | | | | | | | | | | | | | | | | |
| | ☐ A Secret Home | | | | | | | | | | | | | | | | | | | | | | |
| | P ☐ Animal Instincts | | | | | | | | | | | | | | | | | | | | | | |
| | ☐ Plenty of Pets | | | | | | | | | | | | | | | | | | | | | | |
| | O ☐ Snake Myths | | | | | | | | | | | | | | | | | | | | | | |
| | ☐ The New Girl | | | | | | | | | | | | | | | | | | | | | | |
| | N ☐ Dogs at Work | | | | | | | | | | | | | | | | | | | | | | |
| | ☐ Vanessa's Butterfly | | | | | | | | | | | | | | | | | | | | | | |
| | M ☐ City Hawks | | | | | | | | | | | | | | | | | | | | | | |
| | ☐ Saving Up | | | | | | | | | | | | | | | | | | | | | | |
| | L ☐ Baby Monkey | | | | | | | | | | | | | | | | | | | | | | |
| | ☐ Ernie Learns | | | | | | | | | | | | | | | | | | | | | | |
| System 1 | N ☐ Exploring Caves | | | | | | | | | | | | | | | | | | | | | | |
| | ☐ The Big Snow | | | | | | | | | | | | | | | | | | | | | | |
| | M ☐ Monarch Butterfly | | | | | | | | | | | | | | | | | | | | | | |
| | ☐ Thing About Nathan | | | | | | | | | | | | | | | | | | | | | | |
| | L ☐ Giants of the Sea | | | | | | | | | | | | | | | | | | | | | | |
| | ☐ Dog Stories | | | | | | | | | | | | | | | | | | | | | | |
| | K ☐ Animal Senses | | | | | | | | | | | | | | | | | | | | | | |
| | ☐ Edwin's Haircut | | | | | | | | | | | | | | | | | | | | | | |
| | J ☐ More Than a Pet | | | | | | | | | | | | | | | | | | | | | | |
| | ☐ Our New Neighbors | | | | | | | | | | | | | | | | | | | | | | |
| | I ☐ All About Koalas | | | | | | | | | | | | | | | | | | | | | | |
| | ☐ The Best Cat | | | | | | | | | | | | | | | | | | | | | | |
| | H ☐ Trucks | | | | | | | | | | | | | | | | | | | | | | |
| | ☐ The Sleepover Party | | | | | | | | | | | | | | | | | | | | | | |
| | G ☐ Bubbles | | | | | | | | | | | | | | | | | | | | | | |
| | ☐ Bedtime for Nick | | | | | | | | | | | | | | | | | | | | | | |
| | F ☐ From Nest to Bird | | | | | | | | | | | | | | | | | | | | | | |
| | ☐ Anna's New Glasses | | | | | | | | | | | | | | | | | | | | | | |
| | E ☐ The Zoo | | | | | | | | | | | | | | | | | | | | | | |
| | ☐ The Loose Tooth | | | | | | | | | | | | | | | | | | | | | | |
| | D ☐ Mr. Brown | | | | | | | | | | | | | | | | | | | | | | |
| | ☐ Nice Little House | | | | | | | | | | | | | | | | | | | | | | |
| | C ☐ Shopping | | | | | | | | | | | | | | | | | | | | | | |
| | ☐ Socks | | | | | | | | | | | | | | | | | | | | | | |
| | B ☐ Playing | | | | | | | | | | | | | | | | | | | | | | |
| | ☐ My Little Dog | | | | | | | | | | | | | | | | | | | | | | |
| | A ☐ At the Park | | | | | | | | | | | | | | | | | | | | | | |
| | ☐ Best Friends | | | | | | | | | | | | | | | | | | | | | | |
| | **Date** | | | | | | | | | | | | | | | | | | | | | | |
| | **Grade** | | | | K | | 1 | | 2 | | 3 | | 4 | | 5 | | 6 | | 7 | | 8 | |

Summary Forms

# Optional Assessments

The following section includes a variety of useful assessments for the diagnosis of strengths and needs of individuals, small groups, or your whole class. Some of these optional assessments may be required at particular grade levels by your school system. You can photocopy the assessments from this book or print them from the *Forms CD-ROM*.

# Getting Started

In this section, you will find tools to help you determine the starting point for a benchmark assessment conference when you do not have other information such as previous reading records, to help you make a good decision.

# Where-to-Start Word Test

**Description**    Students read a leveled word list.

**You Need**
- ▶ The Where-to-Start Word List
- ▶ The Where-to-Start Chart to determine the level at which to start Benchmark Assessment
- ▶ Where-to-Start Individual Record form

**Why Use It**    If you do not have or are not confident about reading performance information about a child, this quick assessment will give you a broad notion of the level at which to begin Benchmark Assessment.

**How to Use It**

- ▶ Ask the student to read the list for the level below his/her grade level (e.g., kindergarteners and first graders should begin with the **Beginning** list, second graders with the **Level 1** list, fourth graders with the **Level 3** list, etc.).

- ▶ *"I want you to read some words. When you come to a hard word, try it. If you cannot read it, go on to the next word. I'll be making notes while you read. Start here."*

- ▶ Place a card under the first word in the appropriate word list. Have the child move the card down the list as he reads. If the student spends too much time on a word (more than 5 seconds), say *"Read the next one."*

- ▶ As the student reads, score and record word reading on a copy of the list:

  1. Check each word read accurately, including correct guesses, self-corrected readings, and accepted local variations in pronunciation.
  2. Write incorrect responses next to each word. If word not attempted, leave the space blank.
  3. Score as errors words that the student
     - cannot read
     - substitutes with another word or other sounds
     - says several different ways and is uncertain of the correct pronunciation
     - reads incompletely (*bed* instead of *beds*) or adds sounds to (*plays* instead of *play*)
  4. Do not prompt, coach, or ask the student to repeat a word (unless you could not hear it).
  5. Record the number of words read accurately at the bottom of each list.

If the child reads 16 to 20 words on a list correctly, then go to the next level. If a child reads less than 16 words correctly, then stop and begin the text reading at the appropriate level shown on the chart below.

## Where-to-Start Chart

| Number Correct | List Read | | | | |
|---|---|---|---|---|---|
| | **Beginning** | **Level 1** | **Level 2** | **Level 3** | **Level 4** |
| 0–5 | A | A | E | I | M |
| 6–10 | A | B | F | J | M |
| 11–15 | A | C | G | K | N |
| 16–20 | B | D | H | L | N |

## Beginning Word List

| | |
|---|---|
| me | mom |
| I | the |
| can | and |
| to | he |
| my | look |
| we | is |
| in | see |
| like | come |
| it | get |
| up | at |

Getting Started

## Level 1 Word List

| | |
|---|---|
| jump | play |
| here | was |
| little | bike |
| went | with |
| has | they |
| girl | this |
| will | bed |
| have | feet |
| ball | one |
| make | said |

## Level 2 Word List

| | |
|---|---|
| want | morning |
| friend | three |
| puppy | cool |
| basket | drop |
| could | grass |
| dark | when |
| down | first |
| road | train |
| plant | queen |
| away | scream |

Getting Started

## Level 3 Word List

| | |
|---|---|
| plate | forest |
| year | once |
| noise | scramble |
| under | again |
| twisted | careful |
| giant | breakfast |
| knives | batter |
| what | suddenly |
| around | badge |
| because | village |

## Level 4 Word List

| | |
|---|---|
| silence | plastic |
| serious | ocean |
| nature | perform |
| station | delicious |
| graceful | pebble |
| heavy | understood |
| against | destiny |
| excuse | future |
| traffic | anger |
| reward | honey |

Getting Started

# Where-to-Start Word Test—Individual Record

Name _____ Date _____

| Beginning | | Level 1 | | Level 2 | |
|---|---|---|---|---|---|
| me | | jump | | want | |
| I | | here | | friend | |
| can | | little | | puppy | |
| to | | went | | basket | |
| my | | has | | could | |
| we | | girl | | dark | |
| in | | will | | down | |
| like | | have | | road | |
| it | | ball | | plant | |
| up | | make | | away | |
| mom | | play | | morning | |
| the | | was | | three | |
| and | | bike | | cool | |
| he | | with | | drop | |
| look | | they | | grass | |
| is | | this | | when | |
| see | | bed | | first | |
| come | | feet | | train | |
| get | | one | | queen | |
| at | | said | | scream | |
| | **/20** | | **/20** | | **/20** |

# Where-to-Start Word Test—Individual Record

Name _____     Date _____

| Level 3 | | Level 4 | |
|---|---|---|---|
| plate | | silence | |
| year | | serious | |
| noise | | nature | |
| under | | station | |
| twisted | | graceful | |
| giant | | heavy | |
| knives | | against | |
| what | | excuse | |
| around | | traffic | |
| because | | reward | |
| forest | | plastic | |
| once | | ocean | |
| scramble | | perform | |
| again | | delicious | |
| careful | | pebble | |
| breakfast | | understood | |
| better | | destiny | |
| suddenly | | future | |
| badge | | anger | |
| village | | honey | |
| | **/20** | | **/20** |

Getting Started

# Reading Interview

| | |
|---|---|
| **Description** | ▶ Children answer questions about their reading attitudes, interests, and habits. |
| **You Need** | ▶ Reading Interview sheet |
| **Why Use It** | This assessment will help you learn about children's reading interests; you can use it to help them find titles they'll be interested in reading. It will also serve as a guide to how aware they are of their reading strengths and weaknesses. By looking at the interviews across the entire class, you can gauge which reading experiences would be appropriate for the whole group, and which would be more appropriate for a small group or an individual. |

**How to Use It**

▶ Administer this assessment individually by asking each question and recording the child's responses.

▶ You may administer the assessment to the class by giving each child a copy of the Reading Interview sheet (as appropriate to the grade level). If necessary, read each question aloud. Provide ample time for children to write their responses.

▶ If the assessment is administered to the whole class, you may wish to meet with children individually to discuss their responses.

**What to Notice**

▶ Whether children have a difficult time thinking of books they enjoy

▶ Breadth and width of children's reading experiences, including variety of topics, genres, and authors

▶ Level of awareness of reading strengths and weaknesses

Getting Started

# Reading Interview Sheet

Student _____   Grade _____   Date _____

Teacher _____

Answer each question.

What are some books you have been reading this year?
(last year?)

What kinds of books do you like to read?

Who are some of your favorite authors?

What do you do well as a reader?

What do you want to do better as a reader?

# Assessing Fluency and Phrasing

In this section, you will find a detailed rubric for assessing the multiple dimensions of fluent and phrased reading. Although the Recording Form provides a six-point fluency rubric, you may want to use this rubric to analyze specific aspects of fluency for particular students. You will find practice examples for evaluating fluency on the *Professional Development DVD*.

# Six Dimensions Fluency Rubric

**Description**   Use this form to observe and record a student's oral reading of a Benchmark book or other leveled texts.

**You Need**   ▶ A Benchmark or other book at an appropriate level

▶ The Six Dimensions Fluency Rubric

**Why Use It**   The fluency assessment helps you notice and think about the dimensions of oral reading that a student controls and needs to develop.

**How to Use It**   ▶ Administer this assessment individually.

▶ Have the student read aloud the selected text.

▶ Consider rate, phrasing, pausing, intonation, and stress as separate dimensions and rate each of them from 1 to 4 on the rubric.

▶ Then rate integration, your overall impression of the student's orchestration of all the elements in the reading.

**What to Notice**   ▶ Dimensions of fluency the reader is demonstrating and those neglected

© 2008 by Irene C. Fountas and Gay Su Pinnell. Portsmouth, NH: Heinemann. This page may be photocopied.

Student _____   Date _____

## Six Dimensions Fluency Rubric

**1. Pausing** Pausing refers to the way the reader's voice is guided by punctuation (for example, short breath at a comma; full stop with voice going down at periods and up at question marks; full stop at dashes).

| 1 | 2 | 3 | 4 |
|---|---|---|---|
| Almost no pausing to reflect punctuation or meaning of the text *Needs intensive teaching and/or text not appropriate* | Some pausing to reflect the punctuation and meaning of the text *Needs explicit teaching, prompting, and reinforcing* | Most of the reading evidences appropriate pausing to reflect the punctuation and meaning of the text. *Needs some prompting and reinforcing* | Almost all the reading is characterized by pausing to reflect punctuation and meaning of the text. *Teaching not needed* |

**2. Phrasing** Phrasing refers to the way readers put words together in groups to represent the meaningful units of language. Sometimes phrases are cued by punctuation such as commas, but often they are not. Phrased reading sounds like oral language, though more formal.

| 1 | 2 | 3 | 4 |
|---|---|---|---|
| No evidence of appropriate phrasing during the reading *Needs intensive teaching and/or text not appropriate* | Some evidence of appropriate phrasing during the reading *Needs explicit teaching, prompting, and reinforcing* | Much of the reading evidences appropriate phrasing. *Needs some prompting and reinforcing* | Almost all the reading is appropriately phrased. *Teaching not needed* |

**3. Stress** Stress refers to the emphasis readers place on particular words (louder tone) to reflect the meaning as speakers would do in oral language.

| 1 | 2 | 3 | 4 |
|---|---|---|---|
| Almost no stress on appropriate words to reflect the meaning of the text *Needs intensive teaching and/or text not appropriate* | Some stress on appropriate words to reflect the meaning of the text *Needs explicit teaching, prompting, and reinforcing* | Most of the reading evidences stress on appropriate words to reflect the meaning of the text. *Needs some prompting and reinforcing* | Almost all of the reading is characterized by stress on appropriate words to reflect the meaning of the text. *Teaching not needed* |

**4. Intonation** Intonation refers to the way the reader varies the voice in tone, pitch, and volume to reflect the meaning of the text—sometimes called expression.

| 1 | 2 | 3 | 4 |
|---|---|---|---|
| Almost no variation in voice or tone (pitch) to reflect the meaning of the text *Needs intensive teaching and/or text not appropriate* | Some evidence of variation in voice or tone (pitch) to reflect the meaning of the text *Needs explicit teaching, prompting, and reinforcing* | Most of the reading evidences variation in voice or tone (pitch) to reflect the meaning of the text. *Needs some prompting and reinforcing* | Almost all of the reading evidences variation in voice or tone (pitch) to reflect the meaning of the text. *Teaching not needed* |

**5. Rate** Rate refers to the pace at which a reader moves through the text—not too fast and not too slow. The reader moves along steadily with few slow-downs, stops, or pauses to solve words. If the reader has only a few short pauses for word solving and picks up the pace again, look at the overall rate.

| 1 | 2 | 3 | 4 |
|---|---|---|---|
| Almost no evidence of appropriate rate during the reading *Needs intensive teaching and/or text not appropriate* | Some evidence of appropriate rate during the reading *Needs explicit teaching, prompting, and reinforcing* | Most of the reading evidences appropriate rate. *Needs some prompting and reinforcing* | Almost all of the reading evidences appropriate rate. *Teaching not needed* |

**6. Integration** Integration involves the way a reader consistently and evenly orchestrates rate, phrasing, pausing, intonation, and stress.

| 1 | 2 | 3 | 4 |
|---|---|---|---|
| Almost none of the reading is fluent. *Needs intensive teaching and/or text not appropriate* | Some of the reading is fluent. *Needs explicit teaching, prompting, and reinforcing* | Most of the reading is fluent. *Needs some prompting and reinforcing* | Almost all of the reading is fluent. *Teaching not needed* |

**Guiding Principles for Rating** Try to focus on one aspect at a time but give your overall impression.

Assessing Fluency and Phrasing

# Phonics and Word Analysis Assessments

You can select from the following individual, small group, or whole class assessments to identify strengths and needs in your students' knowledge of letter-sound relationships and in their ability to take words apart. You will also find a variety of forms to help you summarize and analyze the results. Use this information in conjunction with the data you gather in the benchmark assessment conferences.

# Letter Recognition: **Uppercase and Lowercase Naming**

**Description**   Children say the names of the alphabet by recognizing the shapes of uppercase and lowercase letters.

**You Need**
▶ Uppercase Letter Recognition Sheet

▶ Lowercase Letter Recognition Sheet

▶ Letter Recognition Assessment—Individual Record form

▶ Letter Recognition Assessment—Class Record form

**Why Use It**   This assessment will identify letter forms children can associate with the corresponding letter name. Use this information to plan lessons on letters and also to decide what letters and letter features to bring to children's attention during interactive writing or shared reading.

**How to Use It**
▶ Administer this assessment individually. Start with uppercase letters and then assess lowercase letters.

▶ Give the child the Uppercase Letter Recognition Sheet. Cover all but the top row. Point to each letter in the top row and ask the child "What's this?" Once the child understands, have the child continue reading across as you move down the rows. If the child pauses more than three to five seconds, tell the child to go on to the right. Repeat the process with the Lowercase Letter Recognition Sheet.

▶ Record responses on the child's Individual Record.

**What to Notice**
▶ Number of letters named accurately

▶ Unknown letter names

▶ Speed in letter recognition

▶ Letter confusions and substitutions

▶ Sounds known without knowledge of letter names

## Uppercase Letter Recognition Sheet

| | | | |
|---|---|---|---|
| H | E | M | T |
| I | P | Q | U |
| O | C | W | B |
| X | V | J | S |
| G | N | Y | K |
| Z | R | A | F |
| L | D | | |

Phonics & Word Analysis

## Lowercase Letter Recognition Sheet

| | | | |
|---|---|---|---|
| h | e | m | t |
| i | p | q | u |
| o | c | w | b |
| x | v | j | s |
| g | n | y | k |
| z | r | a | f |
| l | d | | |

# Letter Recognition Assessment—**Individual Record**

Name _____ Grade _____ Date _____

Directions: Use Uppercase and Lowercase Letter Recognition Sheets. Slide a card under each letter and ask the child to read it. Check (✓) accurate responses and note substitutions. Calculate number of letters known (as well as total score). Note unknown letters. Evaluate substitutions to determine features to which children are attending.

| Letter | Accurate | Substitution or Confusion |
|--------|----------|---------------------------|
| H | | |
| E | | |
| M | | |
| T | | |
| I | | |
| P | | |
| Q | | |
| U | | |
| O | | |
| C | | |
| W | | |
| B | | |
| X | | |
| V | | |
| J | | |
| S | | |
| G | | |
| N | | |
| Y | | |
| K | | |
| Z | | |
| R | | |
| A | | |
| F | | |
| L | | |
| D | | |
| Score | | |

| Letter | Accurate | Substitution or Confusion |
|--------|----------|---------------------------|
| h | | |
| e | | |
| m | | |
| t | | |
| i | | |
| p | | |
| q | | |
| u | | |
| o | | |
| c | | |
| w | | |
| b | | |
| x | | |
| v | | |
| j | | |
| s | | |
| g | | |
| n | | |
| y | | |
| k | | |
| z | | |
| r | | |
| a | | |
| f | | |
| l | | |
| d | | |
| Score | | |

| Unknown Letters | Substitutions | Total Score for All Letters |
|-----------------|---------------|------------------------------|
| | | |

Phonics & Word Analysis

# Letter Recognition Assessment—**Class Record**

Uppercase and Lowercase Letter Recognition Assessment—Class Record

| Name | Identified 0–10 Uppercase Letters | Identified 11–15 Uppercase Letters | Identified 16–26 Uppercase Letters | Identified 0–10 Lowercase Letters | Identified 11–15 Lowercase Letters | Identified 16–26 Lowercase Letters |
|---|---|---|---|---|---|---|
| 1. | | | | | | |
| 2. | | | | | | |
| 3. | | | | | | |
| 4. | | | | | | |
| 5. | | | | | | |
| 6. | | | | | | |
| 7. | | | | | | |
| 8. | | | | | | |
| 9. | | | | | | |
| 10. | | | | | | |
| 11. | | | | | | |
| 12. | | | | | | |
| 13. | | | | | | |
| 14. | | | | | | |
| 15. | | | | | | |
| 16. | | | | | | |
| 17. | | | | | | |
| 18. | | | | | | |
| 19. | | | | | | |
| 20. | | | | | | |
| 21. | | | | | | |
| 22. | | | | | | |
| 23. | | | | | | |
| 24. | | | | | | |
| 25. | | | | | | |
| 26. | | | | | | |
| 27. | | | | | | |
| 28. | | | | | | |

Phonics & Word Analysis

# Early Literacy Behaviors

**Description**  Children demonstrate that they know and can use the following conventions related to print:

▶ Finding specific words within a text

▶ Matching words they hear with words they read

**You Need**  ▶ Any Level B or C book from the Benchmark Assessment System 1

▶ Early Literacy Behaviors Assessment—Individual Record form

▶ Early Literacy Behaviors Assessment—Class Summary form

**Why Use It**  This assessment will help you learn whether children can think about a specific known word and how it looks and then locate it in a text. You will also learn whether children can think about an unknown word, say it, think about the sounds and letters, and use visual features to find the word within the lines of text.

One key early behavior for the young reader to master is the coordination between spoken and written language. The reader must understand and demonstrate that one spoken word is matched with one printed word (cluster of letters defined by white space). If a child knows where to start reading (on the left) and where to go after that (returning to the left to start a new line), then some important orienting behaviors are under control. If he can point to the words while you read the story, then he is gaining control of the directional behaviors needed for reading.

You will also want to know if the reader can recognize and use letters within print. A reader may learn a letter in isolation and even connect it with a sound, but it is an additional challenge to locate letters that are embedded in print. You will want to know whether the reader can distinguish individual letters by their features and can distinguish between letters and words (clusters of letters). Finally you will learn whether a reader is beginning to notice important graphic signs such as punctuation, which help in parsing language (paragraphs into sentences and sentences into phrases).

All of these understandings are key to the reader's developing an early system for processing print, and they are foundational to taking on and understanding longer texts. The information from this added assessment will guide your teaching in ways that can help emergent readers automatically apply understandings such as left to right directionality and word by word matching.

**How to Use It**  ▶ Select a Level B or C book from the Benchmark Assessment System 1 that you do not plan to use for assessment.

▶ Read the book to the child.

▶ Turn back to the front of the book and look at the second or third page. Ask:

1. Where do I start reading? [The child should point to the left margin on line 1.]

2. Where do I go after that? [The child should point to the left margin on line 2.]

3. Find [word] on this page. [Select a word that the child has recognized on the word test. If no words were recognized, skip this item.]

4. Find [word] on this page. [Have the child locate another known word. If the child does not recognize 2 words, skip this item.]

5. Say [word.] Find [word] on this page. [You may want to turn to another page. Select a word that the child did not recognize on the word test and that begins with a consonant. Have the child say it slowly and then locate it on the page.]

6. Point while I read. [Read the page, asking the child to point. The child should match one spoken word with one word in print.]

7. Find the letter _____. [Have the child locate a letter after you say it.]

8. Find the letter _____. [Have the child locate another letter after you say it.]

9. Find a word that starts with [letter.] [Using any letter, have the child locate a word that starts with it.]

10. What's this? [Point to an ending mark (period or exclamation mark). Ask the child to tell what it means.]

**What to Notice**   As you interact with the child around a simple text, notice:

▶ behaviors that seem quick and automatic

▶ speed in locating words and letters

▶ ability to connect letters, sounds, and words

▶ ability to match one spoken word with one written word

▶ ability to distinguish letter features when they are embedded in words

▶ ability to understand the difference between letters and words

▶ ability to read left to right and return to left margin

# Early Literacy Behaviors Assessment—**Individual Record**

Name _____     Grade _____     Date _____

| | Question/Prompt | Accurate Response | Check |
|---|---|---|---|
| 1 | Where do I start reading? | Points to the left margin on line 1 | |
| 2 | Where do I go after that? | Points to the left margin on line 2 | |
| 3 | Find _____ on this page. | Finds a known word | |
| 4 | Find _____ on this page. | Finds a known word | |
| 5 | Say _____ . Find _____ on this page. | Finds an unknown word after saying it | |
| 6 | Point while I read. | Points, matching word by word, while you read two to four lines of print | |
| 7 | Find the letter _____. | Finds the letter that you say | |
| 8 | Find the letter _____. | Finds the letter that you say | |
| 9 | Find a word that starts with _____. | Finds a word that starts with the letter that you say | |
| 10 | What's this? | Finds an ending mark, either period, question mark, or exclamation point | |
| | | **TOTAL POINTS** | |

Phonics & Word Analysis

## Early Literacy Behaviors Assessment—**Class Summary**

| Name | Total Points | Notes |
|------|--------------|-------|
| 1. | | |
| 2. | | |
| 3. | | |
| 4. | | |
| 5. | | |
| 6. | | |
| 7. | | |
| 8. | | |
| 9. | | |
| 10. | | |
| 11. | | |
| 12. | | |
| 13. | | |
| 14. | | |
| 15. | | |
| 16. | | |
| 17. | | |
| 18. | | |
| 19. | | |
| 20. | | |
| 21. | | |
| 22. | | |
| 23. | | |
| 24. | | |
| 25. | | |
| 26. | | |
| 27. | | |
| 28. | | |

Phonics & Word Analysis

# Reading High Frequency Words: **25 Words**

**Description**    Children read 25 high frequency words.

**You Need**
- ▶ The list of 25 high frequency words
- ▶ 25 High Frequency Words Assessment—Individual Record form
- ▶ 25 High Frequency Words Assessment—Class Record form

**Why Use It**    The assessments on pages 239–259 are designed to give you a range of assessment options depending on student ability. Each of the high frequency assessments includes a greater number of words that gradually increase in difficulty level. You may choose to begin with 25 words and move up through each one, or you can pick the list you think would be most appropriate for your students.

This assessment will give you information about children's general knowledge of easy high frequency words as well as the particular words they know. The substitutions they make will also reveal something about their knowledge of letter/sound relationships and spelling patterns.

**How to Use It**
- ▶ Administer this assessment individually.
- ▶ Ask the child to read down the columns of 25 high frequency words.
- ▶ On the Individual Record form, mark the child's correct responses as well as substitutions.
- ▶ Record the results of the assessment on the child's Individual Record.

**What to Notice**
- ▶ Words the child can read correctly
- ▶ Words the child can read almost correctly
- ▶ Letter/sound relationships the child controls

Phonics & Word Analysis

Read the words:

| | | |
|---|---|---|
| no | so | go |
| is | on | it |
| can | in | do |
| me | up | an |
| you | am | the |
| and | we | my |
| he | like | to |
| at | see | |
| a | I | |

# 25 High Frequency Words Assessment—**Individual Record**

Name _____ Grade _____ Date _____

Directions: Use the high frequency word list. Slide a card under each word and ask the child to read it. Check (✓) accurate responses and note substitutions. Calculate number of known words. Evaluate substitutions to determine features to which children are attending.

| Word | ✓ | Substitution |
|------|---|--------------|
| no | | |
| is | | |
| can | | |
| me | | |
| you | | |
| and | | |
| he | | |
| at | | |
| a | | |
| so | | |
| on | | |
| in | | |
| up | | |
| am | | |
| we | | |
| like | | |
| see | | |
| I | | |
| go | | |
| it | | |
| do | | |
| an | | |
| the | | |
| my | | |
| to | | |
| **Total** | | |

Phonics & Word Analysis

# 25 High Frequency Words Assessment—**Class Record**

**Names of Children**

| | | | | | | | | | | | | | |
|---|---|---|---|---|---|---|---|---|---|---|---|---|---|
| no | | | | | | | | | | | | | |
| is | | | | | | | | | | | | | |
| can | | | | | | | | | | | | | |
| me | | | | | | | | | | | | | |
| you | | | | | | | | | | | | | |
| and | | | | | | | | | | | | | |
| he | | | | | | | | | | | | | |
| at | | | | | | | | | | | | | |
| a | | | | | | | | | | | | | |
| so | | | | | | | | | | | | | |
| on | | | | | | | | | | | | | |
| in | | | | | | | | | | | | | |
| up | | | | | | | | | | | | | |
| am | | | | | | | | | | | | | |
| we | | | | | | | | | | | | | |
| like | | | | | | | | | | | | | |
| see | | | | | | | | | | | | | |
| I | | | | | | | | | | | | | |
| go | | | | | | | | | | | | | |
| it | | | | | | | | | | | | | |
| do | | | | | | | | | | | | | |
| an | | | | | | | | | | | | | |
| the | | | | | | | | | | | | | |
| my | | | | | | | | | | | | | |
| to | | | | | | | | | | | | | |
| **Total** | | | | | | | | | | | | | |

# Reading High Frequency Words: **50 Words**

**Description**   Children read lists of high frequency words.

**You Need**
▶ High Frequency Word List

▶ 50 High Frequency Words Assessment—Individual Record

▶ 50 High Frequency Words Assessment—Class Record

**Why Use It**   The assessments on pages 239–259 are designed to give you a range of assessment options depending on student ability. Each of the high frequency assessments includes a greater number of words that gradually increase in difficulty level. You may choose to begin with 25 words and move up through each one, or you can pick the list you think would be most appropriate for your students.

This assessment will give you information about children's knowledge of high frequency words as well as the particular words they know. If many children miss the same words, it will help you decide which high frequency words to include in lessons and to attend to in reading and writing.

▶ Administer this assessment individually to achieve an inventory of the high frequency words each child knows and the words that will be productive to focus on in teaching. You can administer the assessment in one sitting or have the student do a column of words at a time.

▶ Ask the child to read each word. Record the child's correct responses with a check in the column, and record substitutions if the child misreads the word. If the child makes no response, say, "Try it." If the child still does not respond, leave the box blank. (If a child has difficulty with one out of three words, stop the assessment.)

**What to Notice**
▶ Number of high frequency words read accurately

▶ Specific known words

▶ Words almost known

Phonics & Word Analysis

Read the words:

| | | | |
|---|---|---|---|
| all | girl | not | she |
| are | got | now | sit |
| as | had | of | then |
| ball | has | or | they |
| be | her | out | this |
| boy | him | play | too |
| by | his | put | us |
| come | how | ran | was |
| day | if | read | went |
| did | jump | run | will |
| eat | look | sat | yes |
| for | man | saw | |
| get | mom | say | |

# 50 High Frequency Words Assessment—**Individual Record**

Name _____ Grade _____ Date _____

Directions: Use the high frequency word list. Slide a card under each word and ask the child to read it. Check (✓) accurate responses and note substitutions. Calculate number of known words. Evaluate substitutions to determine features to which children are attending.

© 2008 by Irene C. Fountas and Gay Su Pinnell. Portsmouth, NH: Heinemann. This page may be photocopied.

| Word | ✓ | Substitution |
|------|---|--------------|
| all | | |
| are | | |
| as | | |
| ball | | |
| be | | |
| boy | | |
| by | | |
| come | | |
| day | | |
| did | | |
| eat | | |
| for | | |
| get | | |
| girl | | |
| got | | |
| had | | |
| has | | |
| her | | |
| him | | |
| his | | |
| how | | |
| if | | |
| jump | | |
| look | | |
| man | | |
| **Subtotal** | | |

| Word | ✓ | Substitution |
|------|---|--------------|
| mom | | |
| not | | |
| now | | |
| of | | |
| or | | |
| out | | |
| play | | |
| put | | |
| ran | | |
| read | | |
| run | | |
| sat | | |
| saw | | |
| say | | |
| she | | |
| sit | | |
| then | | |
| they | | |
| this | | |
| too | | |
| us | | |
| was | | |
| went | | |
| will | | |
| yes | | |
| **Subtotal** | | |

**Total number of known words:** _____

# 50 High Frequency Words Assessment—**Class Record**

| Name | Total number of known words |
|---|---|
| **1.** | |
| **2.** | |
| **3.** | |
| **4.** | |
| **5.** | |
| **6.** | |
| **7.** | |
| **8.** | |
| **9.** | |
| **10.** | |
| **11.** | |
| **12.** | |
| **13.** | |
| **14.** | |
| **15.** | |
| **16.** | |
| **17.** | |
| **18.** | |
| **19.** | |
| **20.** | |
| **21.** | |
| **22.** | |
| **23.** | |
| **24.** | |
| **25.** | |
| **26.** | |
| **27.** | |
| **28.** | |

Notes

# Reading High Frequency Words: **100 Words**

**Description** Children read a list of high frequency words.

**You Need**
▶ 100 High Frequency Words, Lists 1, 2, 3, 4, and 5
▶ 100 High Frequency Words Assessment—Individual Record form
▶ 100 High Frequency Words Assessment—Class Record form

**Why Use It** The assessments on pages 239–259 are designed to give you a range of assessment options depending on student ability. Each of the high frequency assessments includes a greater number of words that gradually increase in difficulty level. You may choose to begin with 25 words and move up through each one, or you can pick the list you think would be most appropriate for your students.

This assessment will tell you the extent of the children's knowledge of high frequency words as well as the particular words they know. Their substitutions will tell you what word parts they notice.

*Children need to be able to read a large number of high frequency words. However, don't build your phonics and word-solving program around memorizing words; using patterns and parts (for example, using phonograms, letter clusters, and affixes) are more powerful strategies.*

**How to Use It**
▶ Administer this test individually.
▶ Begin with the 45 easier high frequency words included on Lists 1, 2, and 3. Work with one list at a time. If you think they are very easy, use the 55 additional high frequency words on Lists 4 and 5. If these words are still too easy for your children, move to the next assessment.
▶ Ask the child to read the list of words you've selected.
▶ Children should be able to read the list quickly. Don't spend too much time on any word; tell the child to skip it and go on. If children are missing or refusing to attempt a large number of words, suggest they look down the list to see if there are any they know or stop the assessment.
▶ Record the child's correct responses as well as substitutions on the Individual Record form.

**What to Notice**
▶ Number of high frequency words read accurately
▶ Speed of word recognition
▶ Partially correct attempts or parts of words known
▶ Degree of difficulty of known words

**Phonics & Word Analysis**

## 100 High Frequency Words, **page 1**

Read the words:

| List 1 | List 2 | List 3 |
| --- | --- | --- |
| than | have | over |
| about | there | ride |
| back | any | don't |
| after | into | said |
| I'm | just | that |
| been | little | one |
| big | make | with |
| came | before | five |
| away | two | their |
| your | four | what |
| who | mother | but |
| when | where | here |
| them | very | going |
| because | could | our |
| from | were | three |

## 100 High Frequency Words, **page 2**

Read the words:

| List 4 | | List 5 | |
|--------|--------|--------|--------|
| want | take | books | sleep |
| able | dad | good | love |
| bad | hide | help | much |
| give | almost | city | stay |
| today | dog | write | name |
| week | anything | top | new |
| something | home | room | paper |
| bus | down | under | rain |
| year | become | fast | door |
| can't | end | hill | fun |
| tell | behind | know | sky |
| across | fish | use | both |
| world | why | let | time |
| cat | car | place | |

Phonics & Word Analysis

# 100 High Frequency Words Assessment—**Individual Record**

Name _____ Grade _____ Date _____

Directions: Use the most appropriate high frequency word list. Ask the child to read each word. Check (✓) accurate responses and note substitutions. Calculate number of known words. Evaluate substitutions to determine features to which children are attending.

| List 1 | ✓or write substitution | | List 2 | ✓or write substitution | | List 3 | ✓or write substitution |
|---|---|---|---|---|---|---|---|
| than | | | have | | | over | |
| about | | | there | | | ride | |
| back | | | any | | | don't | |
| after | | | into | | | said | |
| I'm | | | just | | | that | |
| been | | | little | | | one | |
| big | | | make | | | with | |
| came | | | before | | | five | |
| away | | | two | | | their | |
| your | | | four | | | what | |
| who | | | mother | | | but | |
| when | | | where | | | here | |
| them | | | very | | | going | |
| because | | | could | | | our | |
| from | | | were | | | three | |
| **Subtotal** | | | **Subtotal** | | | **Subtotal** | |

**Total number of known words:** _____

## 100 High Frequency Words Assessment—**Individual Record** *continued*

© 2008 by Irene C. Fountas and Gay Su Pinnell. Portsmouth, NH: Heinemann. This page may be photocopied.

| List 4 | ✓or write substitution |
|---|---|
| want | |
| able | |
| bad | |
| give | |
| today | |
| week | |
| something | |
| bus | |
| year | |
| can't | |
| tell | |
| across | |
| world | |
| cat | |
| take | |
| dad | |
| hide | |
| almost | |
| dog | |
| anything | |
| home | |
| down | |
| become | |
| end | |
| behind | |
| fish | |
| why | |
| car | |
| **Subtotal** | |

| List 5 | ✓or write substitution |
|---|---|
| books | |
| good | |
| help | |
| city | |
| write | |
| top | |
| room | |
| under | |
| fast | |
| hill | |
| know | |
| use | |
| let | |
| place | |
| sleep | |
| love | |
| much | |
| stay | |
| name | |
| new | |
| paper | |
| rain | |
| door | |
| fun | |
| sky | |
| both | |
| time | |
| **Subtotal** | |

**Total number of known words:** _____

Phonics & Word Analysis

# 100 High Frequency Words Assessment—**Class Record**

| Name | Total number of known words |
|---|---|
| 1. | |
| 2. | |
| 3. | |
| 4. | |
| 5. | |
| 6. | |
| 7. | |
| 8. | |
| 9. | |
| 10. | |
| 11. | |
| 12. | |
| 13. | |
| 14. | |
| 15. | |
| 16. | |
| 17. | |
| 18. | |
| 19. | |
| 20. | |
| 21. | |
| 22. | |
| 23. | |
| 24. | |
| 25. | |
| 26. | |
| 27. | |
| 28. | |

Notes

Phonics & Word Analysis

# Reading High Frequency Words: **200 Words**

**Description**  Children read a list of high frequency words.

**You Need**
- 200 High Frequency Words, Lists 1, 2, 3, 4, and 5
- 200 High Frequency Words Assessment—Individual Record form
- 200 High Frequency Words Assessment—Class Record form

**Why Use It**  The assessments on pages 239–259 are designed to give you a range of assessment options depending on student ability. Each of the high frequency assessments includes a greater number of words that gradually increase in difficulty level. You may choose to begin with 25 words and move up through each one, or you can pick the list you think would be most appropriate for your students.

This assessment will tell you the extent of the children's knowledge of high frequency words as well as the particular words they know. Their substitutions will tell you what word parts they notice.

*Children need to be able to read a large number of high frequency words. However, don't build your phonics and word-solving program around memorizing words; using patterns and parts (for example, using phonograms, letter clusters, and affixes) are more powerful strategies.*

**How to Use It**
- Administer this test individually.
- Begin with the 80 easier high frequency words included on Lists 1, 2, and 3. Work with one list at a time. If you think they are very easy, use the 120 additional high frequency words on Lists 4 and 5.
- Ask the child to read the list of words you've selected.
- Children should be able to read the list quickly. Don't spend too much time on any word; tell the child to skip it and go on. If children are missing or refusing to attempt a large number of words, suggest they look down the list to see if there are any they know or stop the assessment.
- Record the child's correct responses as well as substitutions on the Individual Record form.

**What to Notice**
- Number of high frequency words read accurately
- Speed of word recognition
- Partially correct attempts or parts of words known
- Degree of difficulty of known words

Phonics & Word Analysis

## 200 High Frequency Words, **page 1**

Read the words:

| List 1 | List 2 | List 3 |
|--------|--------|--------|
| sea | happy | house |
| wrote | catch | start |
| again | third | grew |
| carry | night | way |
| wait | goes | friend |
| each | last | story |
| feel | school | street |
| always | walk | above |
| first | ten | find |
| ask | change | between |
| food | outside | every |
| work | part | should |
| brother | live | father |
| through | party | watch |
| funny | game | children |
| gave | try | hid |
| things | pick | enough |
| close | right | dark |
| even | teach | great |
| grow | until | inside |
| gone | second | light |
| same | deep | seen |
| knew | view | during |
| begin | grade | worn |
| winter | snow | wrong |
| must | does | you're |
| stop | together | |

Phonics & Word Analysis

## 200 High Frequency Words, **page 2**

Read the words:

| List 4 | | List 5 | |
|---|---|---|---|
| several | river | follow | being |
| never | might | pretty | also |
| getting | air | couldn't | slowly |
| earth | I'd | happen | bring |
| group | suddenly | themselves | hear |
| baby | easy | direction | often |
| everything | finally | nothing | page |
| high | everyone | life | store |
| wouldn't | hold | someone | while |
| probably | special | without | however |
| through | animal | instead | kids |
| against | lost | either | check |
| hour | beautiful | lunch | listen |
| fight | need | important | few |
| once | job | less | stuff |
| best | sick | own | problem |
| ready | maybe | think | such |
| free | land | round | cleans |
| show | next | scared | teacher |
| build | old | person | dream |
| draw | window | short | sister |
| state | better | add | plan |
| kind | written | wanted | they're |
| circle | favorite | young | possible |
| large | care | question | thought |
| doing | myself | yourself | really |
| family | since | answer | understand |
| clothes | picture | money | near |
| hand | class | simple | rest |
| different | idea | more | soon |

Phonics & Word Analysis

# 200 High Frequency Words Assessment—**Individual Record, page 1**

Name _____ Grade _____ Date _____

Directions: Use the most appropriate high frequency word list. Ask the child to read each word. Check (✓) accurate responses and note substitutions. Calculate number of known words. Evaluate substitutions to determine features to which children are attending.

| List 1 | ✓ or write substitution | List 2 | ✓ or write substitution | List 3 | ✓ or write substitution |
|---|---|---|---|---|---|
| sea | | happy | | house | |
| wrote | | catch | | start | |
| again | | third | | grew | |
| carry | | night | | way | |
| wait | | goes | | friend | |
| each | | last | | story | |
| feel | | school | | street | |
| always | | walk | | above | |
| first | | ten | | find | |
| ask | | change | | between | |
| food | | outside | | every | |
| work | | part | | should | |
| brother | | live | | father | |
| through | | party | | watch | |
| funny | | game | | children | |
| gave | | try | | hid | |
| things | | pick | | enough | |
| close | | right | | dark | |
| even | | teach | | great | |
| grow | | until | | inside | |
| gone | | second | | light | |
| same | | deep | | seen | |
| knew | | view | | during | |
| begin | | grade | | worn | |
| winter | | snow | | wrong | |
| must | | does | | you're | |
| stop | | together | | | |
| **Subtotal** | | **Subtotal** | | **Subtotal** | |

**Total number of known words:** _____

# 200 High Frequency Words Assessment—**Individual Record, page 2**

| List 4 | ✓ or write substitution | List 4 | ✓ or write substitution |
|---|---|---|---|
| several | | river | |
| never | | might | |
| getting | | air | |
| earth | | I'd | |
| group | | suddenly | |
| baby | | easy | |
| everything | | finally | |
| high | | everyone | |
| wouldn't | | hold | |
| probably | | special | |
| through | | animal | |
| against | | lost | |
| hour | | beautiful | |
| fight | | need | |
| once | | job | |
| best | | sick | |
| ready | | maybe | |
| free | | land | |
| show | | next | |
| build | | old | |
| draw | | window | |
| state | | better | |
| kind | | written | |
| circle | | favorite | |
| large | | care | |
| doing | | myself | |
| family | | since | |
| clothes | | picture | |
| hand | | class | |
| different | | idea | |
| **Subtotal** | | **Subtotal** | |

**Total number of known words:** _____

Phonics & Word Analysis

# 200 High Frequency Words Assessment—**Individual Record, page 3**

| List 5 | ✓ or write substitution | List 5 | ✓ or write substitution |
|---|---|---|---|
| follow | | being | |
| pretty | | also | |
| couldn't | | slowly | |
| happen | | bring | |
| themselves | | hear | |
| direction | | often | |
| nothing | | page | |
| life | | store | |
| someone | | while | |
| without | | however | |
| instead | | kids | |
| either | | check | |
| lunch | | listen | |
| important | | few | |
| less | | stuff | |
| own | | problem | |
| think | | such | |
| round | | cleans | |
| scared | | teacher | |
| person | | dream | |
| short | | sister | |
| add | | plan | |
| wanted | | they're | |
| young | | possible | |
| question | | thought | |
| yourself | | really | |
| answer | | understand | |
| money | | near | |
| simple | | rest | |
| more | | soon | |
| **Subtotal** | | **Subtotal** | |

**Total number of known words:** _____

## 200 High Frequency Words Assessment—**Class Record**

| Name | Total number of known words |
|---|---|
| 1. | |
| 2. | |
| 3. | |
| 4. | |
| 5. | |
| 6. | |
| 7. | |
| 8. | |
| 9. | |
| 10. | |
| 11. | |
| 12. | |
| 13. | |
| 14. | |
| 15. | |
| 16. | |
| 17. | |
| 18. | |
| 19. | |
| 20. | |
| 21. | |
| 22. | |
| 23. | |
| 24. | |
| 25. | |
| 26. | |
| 27. | |
| 28. | |

Notes

Phonics & Word Analysis

# Phonological Awareness: **Initial Sounds**

**Description**   Children identify pictures with the same initial sound as a spoken word.

Children are given four picture cards and told the name of each picture. They say the sound and point to or say the picture that begins with the same sound. The child is also asked to produce orally the beginning sound for an orally presented word that matches one of the given pictures.

**You Need**
▶ Initial Sounds Picture Cards—Sheets 1 and 2
▶ Phonological Awareness Assessment—Individual Record form
▶ Phonological Awareness Assessment—Class Record form

**Why Use It**   This assessment will tell you whether children can hear and match initial sounds in words.

**How to Use It**
▶ Administer this test individually.
▶ Begin by showing the child four picture cards: *bear*, *hat*, *dog*, and *milk*. Say the name of each picture. Then hold up the picture card for *bird*, say the name, and ask the child to find the other picture card that starts with the same sound. Repeat using *horse, desk,* and *mouse*.
▶ Then, say the name of four of the pictures: *bird, horse, desk,* and *mouse* and ask the child to orally produce the initial sound.
▶ Record the child's correct responses as well as substitutions on the Individual Record form.
▶ Show the child four more picture cards: *cat, fan, ladder,* and *pencil.* Say the name of each picture. Use *cake, fire, lion,* and *penguin* and ask the child to find the other picture card that starts with the same sound.
▶ Then, say the names: *cake, fire, lion,* and *penguin.* Ask the child to orally produce the initial sound.
▶ Record the child's correct responses as well as substitutions on the Individual Record form.

**What to Notice**
▶ Number of sounds the child can correctly match
▶ Whether children can orally produce the initial sound of a word they have heard

## Initial Sounds Picture Cards—**Sheet 1**

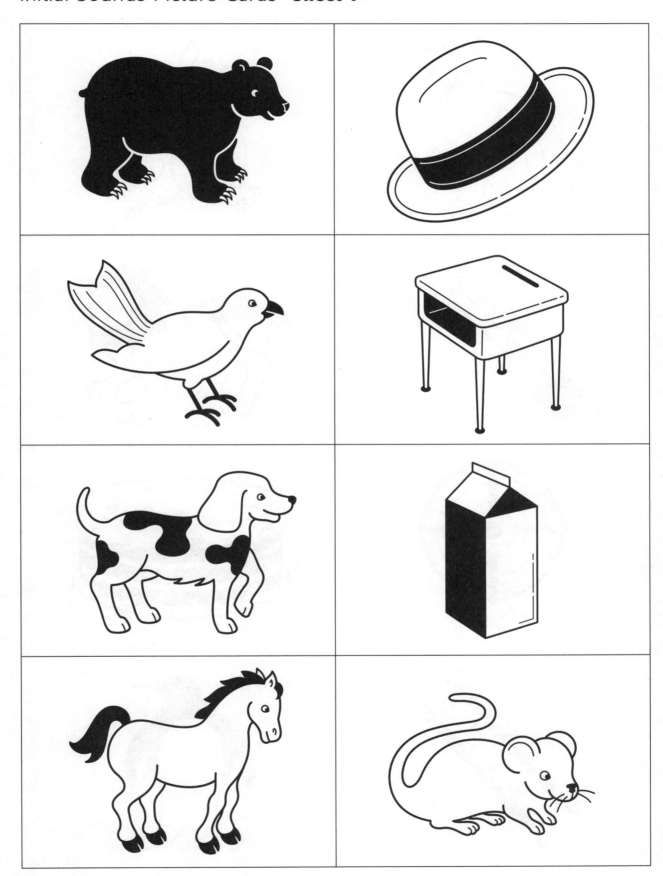

Phonics & Word Analysis

## Initial Sounds Picture Cards—**Sheet 2**

# Phonological Awareness: **Blending Words**

**Description**     Children hear and say the individual sounds in a word and then blend the sounds to say the word.

**You Need**     ▶ Phonological Awareness Assessment—Individual Record form

▶ Phonological Awareness Assessment—Class Record form

**Why Use It**     This assessment will help you learn whether children can take individual sounds and blend them together. This ability helps children take words apart to solve them. Some children will grasp this principle with only a few demonstrations. Use this assessment to determine how much experience children need in blending sounds.

**How to Use It**     ▶ Administer this task individually so you can closely observe behavior. Tell the child you are going to say the sounds of a word: "I will say the sounds of a word. Then you say the whole word smoothly." Use /m/-/ă/-/t/, *mat*, as an example. Continue with:

/h/-/ĭ/-/d/ [hid]

/w/-/ĭ/-/sh/ [wish]

/p/-/ŏ/-/t/ [pot]

/f/-/ē/-/t/ [feet]

/l/-/o͝o /-/k/ [look]

/t/-/ā/-/k/ [take]

/m/-/o͞o/-/n/ [moon]

/n/-/ŭ/-/t/ [nut]

/r/-/ă/-/p/ [rap]

/ch/-/ĭ/-/l/ [chill]

▶ Record results on the child's Individual Record. Consider the task mastered if a child can blend eight of the ten words.

**What to Notice**     ▶ Ability to listen to and understand the task

▶ Ability to blend the sounds

Phonics & Word Analysis

# Phonological Awareness: **Segmenting Words**

**Description**    Children say a word and then say the individual sounds separately but in sequence.

**You Need**

▶ Phonological Awareness Assessment—Individual Record form

▶ Phonological Awareness Assessment—Class Record form

**Why Use It**    This assessment will help you learn whether children can take a word and segment it into individual sounds. This ability helps children in both spelling and decoding. Some children may understand this principle with only a few demonstrations. Others will need more experience.

**How to Use It**   ▶ Administer this assessment individually so you can closely observe behavior. Say the word and ask the child to say the segmented sounds in the word: "I am going to say a word. Then you say the sounds in the word, like this: *fan*, /f/-/ă/-/n/." Then continue with:

*wet* [/w/-/ĕ/-/t/]

*vase* [/v/-/ā/-/s/]

*trip* [/t/-/r/-/ĭ/-/p/]

*miss* [/m/-/ĭ/-/s/]

*duck* [/d/-/ŭ/-/k/]

*pad* [/p/-/ă/-/d/]

*fast* /f/-/ă/-/s/-/t/]

*kick* [/k/-/ĭ/-/k/]

*tool* [/t/-/o͞o/-/l/]

*boat* [/b/-/ō/-/t/]

▶ Record results on the child's Individual Record. Consider the task mastered if a child can segment eight of the ten words.

**What to Notice**   ▶ Ability to listen to and understand the task

▶ Ability to say each sound

▶ Ability to say sounds in sequence

# Phonological Awareness: **Rhyming**

**Description**    Children match words that sound alike in the ending part (rime).

**You Need**
- ▶ Rhyming Cards—Sheets 1 and 2
- ▶ Phonological Awareness Assessment—Individual Record form
- ▶ Phonological Awareness Assessment—Class Record form

**Why Use It**    This assessment will help you learn the degree to which children can hear and make connections between words that rhyme. Recognizing rhymes is foundational to recognizing word parts and beginning to analyze words.

**How to Use It**
- ▶ Have children match picture cards representing pairs of words that rhyme, saying the words to check them. Start by demonstrating with one or two easy examples to help children understand the task. Sample words are *bee, tree; fish, dish; fan, van; box, socks; star, car*.

- ▶ Administering the assessment individually will not take much time and will give you important insight into the child's processing. For example, a child who connects *fish* and *fan* is making a good sound analysis that does not meet the requirements of the task. You can intervene with a few examples of rhymes (noting your support on the record sheet) to see whether he now grasps the idea or continues to be confused.

- ▶ Record each child's responses on the Individual Record form. There is enough space for a longer test, but you do not need many items to get an idea of whether the child understands the concept.

**What to Notice**
- ▶ Ability to identify and say labels of objects represented in pictures
- ▶ Ability to listen for and identify sound patterns (rhymes) in words
- ▶ Ability to connect a sound pattern with another sound pattern that is similar
- ▶ Speed with which the child identifies similar sound patterns (rhymes)

Phonics & Word Analysis

# Rhyming Cards—**Sheet 1**

Name _____

Match the rhymes.

# Rhyming Cards—**Sheet 2**

Name _____

Match the rhymes.

Phonics & Word Analysis

# Phonological Awareness Assessment—**Individual Record**

Name _____  Grade _____  Date _____

### Initial Sounds Assessment

| | Matching (✓ or substitutions) | Oral (✓ or substitutions) |
|---|---|---|
| b /b/ | | |
| h /h/ | | |
| d /d/ | | |
| m /m/ | | |
| c /k/ | | |
| f /f/ | | |
| l /l/ | | |
| p /p/ | | |
| **Total** | | |

### Blending Assessment

| | Scoring (✓) |
|---|---|
| /h/-/ĭ/-/d/ [hid] | |
| /w/-/ĭ/-/sh/ [wish] | |
| /p/-/ŏ/-/t/ [pot] | |
| /f/-/ē/-/t/ [feet] | |
| /l/-/o͞o/-/k/ [look] | |
| /t/-/ā/-/k/ [take] | |
| /m/-/o͞o/-/n/ [moon] | |
| /n/-/ŭ/-/t/ [nut] | |
| /r/-/ă/-/p/ [rap] | |
| /ch/-/ĭ/-/l/ [chill] | |
| **Total** | |

### Segmenting Assessment

| | Scoring (✓) |
|---|---|
| wet [/w/-/ĕ/-/t/] | |
| vase [/v/-/ā/-/s/] | |
| trip [/t/-/r/-/ĭ/-/p/] | |
| miss [/m/-/ĭ/-/s/] | |
| duck [/d/-/ŭ/-/k/] | |
| pad [/p/-/ă/-/d/] | |
| fast [/f/-/ă/-/s/-/t/] | |
| kick [/k/-/ĭ/-/k/] | |
| tool [/t/-/o͞o/-/l/] | |
| boat [/b/-/ō/-/t/] | |
| **Total** | |

### Rhyming Assessment

| | Scoring (✓) |
|---|---|
| bee/tree | |
| fish/dish | |
| fan/van | |
| box/socks | |
| star/car | |
| rose/nose | |
| pen/hen | |
| bat/hat | |
| crown/clown | |
| ring/swing | |
| **Total** | |

# Phonological Awareness Assessment—**Class Record**

| Name | Initial Sounds Assessment | Blending Assessment | Segmenting Assessment | Rhyming Assessment |
|---|---|---|---|---|
| 1. | | | | |
| 2. | | | | |
| 3. | | | | |
| 4. | | | | |
| 5. | | | | |
| 6. | | | | |
| 7. | | | | |
| 8. | | | | |
| 9. | | | | |
| 10. | | | | |
| 11. | | | | |
| 12. | | | | |
| 13. | | | | |
| 14. | | | | |
| 15. | | | | |
| 16. | | | | |
| 17. | | | | |
| 18. | | | | |
| 19. | | | | |
| 20. | | | | |
| 21. | | | | |
| 22. | | | | |
| 23. | | | | |
| 24. | | | | |
| 25. | | | | |
| 26. | | | | |
| 27. | | | | |

Notes

Phonics & Word Analysis

# Word Writing

**Description**   Children write all of the words they can write within a designated time limit.

**You Need**
▶ Blank paper with a space for children to write their name.

▶ Word Writing—Class Record form

**Why Use It**   This assessment will give you a rich inventory of what children control in terms of writing. Examining this document will not only tell you the words that children can spell accurately, but also what they are thinking about words and how they work. You can note attempts as well as evidence that children are placing words into categories. You can think about how their strengths in writing words can support reading.

**How to Use It**
▶ Early in the year, you may want to administer this assessment individually so that you can prompt children with familiar words, for example *I, the, it, is, in* (refer to the high frequency word lists on pages 239–259).

▶ At your signal, children write their names and then write all the words they know until you say stop. (Give them between five and ten minutes.) Encourage children to try words even if they think they don't know how to spell them with all the letters.

▶ Suggested language: "We are going to do something special today. Each of you is going to write as many words as you can. Are you thinking of a word you know you can write?" Get some suggestions from the children. "Start by writing your name on the line at the top of the page." Give children time to write their name. "Write words carefully. If you are not sure how to write a word, just try it. Try to leave spaces between your words so that I can read them."

▶ Early in the year, make this assessment informal. You do not need to hide the print on the walls. In fact, it will be interesting to note how children are using the resources in the classroom. Midyear or later, you may want to make assessment more challenging by being sure that children perform the task without access to print on the walls.

▶ Analyze the child's writing to notice what letter/sound relationships and spelling patterns the child controls.

**What to Notice**
▶ Awareness of his own inventory of words

- Knowledge of the way one word leads to another, revealing connections between words as well as categories
- Use of phonograms and spelling patterns
- Ease and fluency in constructing words
- Use of endings to make several words from a root word
- Ability to hear the sounds in words
- Ability to represent sounds with letters
- Knowledge of high frequency word patterns
- Ability to use and connect word parts

# Word Writing

An example of one child's writing is included below. Michael has a score of 59 accurately written words. In addition, notice that he:

▶ has many different ways of getting to words.

▶ began with his name and then wrote another name he knew.

▶ wrote simple, high frequency words in the first column but seemed to connect them because of similar patterns (*in, is, it; there, here*).

▶ added *s* to *book*, making another word, as well as adding *ing* and *ed* to *play*.

▶ wrote *good* and then thought of *go*, perhaps noting their similarity visually.

▶ wrote *you* and then *your*.

▶ wrote *into* and then wrote two other forms of the word *to*, which he wrote instantly because he knew them.

▶ constructed some words without having to think about sounds and letters.

▶ added *d* to *see* to produce *seed*.

▶ made one attempt that resulted in inaccurate spelling—*ttat* for *that*, which may have been the result of hurrying or not noticing (he knows how to use *th* because he spelled *that* correctly later in the sequence, after *them, they,* and *then*).

# Word Writing—**Class Record**

| Name | Total words | Notes |
|---|---|---|
| 1. | | |
| 2. | | |
| 3. | | |
| 4. | | |
| 5. | | |
| 6. | | |
| 7. | | |
| 8. | | |
| 9. | | |
| 10. | | |
| 11. | | |
| 12. | | |
| 13. | | |
| 14. | | |
| 15. | | |
| 16. | | |
| 17. | | |
| 18. | | |
| 19. | | |
| 20. | | |
| 21. | | |
| 22. | | |
| 23. | | |
| 24. | | |
| 25. | | |
| 26. | | |
| 27. | | |
| 28. | | |

Phonics & Word Analysis

# Writing Picture Names

**Description**    Children say words slowly and write the sounds they hear.

**You Need**    ▶ Writing Picture Names—Sheets 1 and 2

▶ Writing Picture Names Assessment—Class Record form

**Why Use It**    This assessment will give you information about whether children can say words slowly, think about the sounds in the words, and record some of them by remembering and writing associated letters. These are complex sets of information. Children are being asked to say and hear a sound, associate it with a letter and the directional movements needed to write the letter, and then use these movements to write the letter in a legible form.

**How to Use It**    ▶ Ask children to attempt to write the letters in a series of words that you say as you hold up a picture card that represents the word. Suggested words:

1. *cat* (three phonemes), *mug* (three phonemes), *nine* (three phonemes), *bed* (three phonemes), *lock* (three phonemes), *desk* (four phonemes), *pin* (three phonemes), and *doll* (three phonemes).

2. *truck* (four phonemes), *feet* (three phonemes), *bag* (three phonemes), *five* (three phonemes), *nose* (three phonemes), *gum* (three phonemes), *map* (three phonemes), and *seal* (three phonemes).

▶ Record the number of different phonemes that each child can represent, for a maximum score of 25 on each list, on the Class Record.

**What to Notice**    ▶ Ability to identify labels for objects represented by pictures

▶ Ability to say words very slowly, to hear each of the sounds

▶ Ability to say, hear, and identify the individual sounds in words

▶ Ability to form letters

▶ The sequence of sounds the child hears and records

Phonics & Word Analysis

## Writing Picture Names, sheet 1

_____

_____

_____

_____

_____

_____

_____

_____

## Writing Picture Names, sheet 2

_____

_____

_____

_____

Phonics & Word Analysis

# Writing Picture Names Assessment—**Class Record**

Date _____

| Name | Writing Words List 1 (max = 25) | Writing Words List 2 (max = 25) |
|---|---|---|
| 1. | | |
| 2. | | |
| 3. | | |
| 4. | | |
| 5. | | |
| 6. | | |
| 7. | | |
| 8. | | |
| 9. | | |
| 10. | | |
| 11. | | |
| 12. | | |
| 13. | | |
| 14. | | |
| 15. | | |
| 16. | | |
| 17. | | |
| 18. | | |
| 19. | | |
| 20. | | |
| 21. | | |
| 22. | | |
| 23. | | |
| 24. | | |
| 25. | | |
| 26. | | |
| 27. | | |
| 28. | | |

Phonics & Word Analysis

# Phonograms

**Description**  Children read words with simple phonogram patterns.

**You Need**
▶ Word Cards made from the Phonogram Word Lists
▶ Phonograms Assessment—Individual Record form
▶ Phonograms Assessment—Class Record form

**Why Use It**  Regular phonogram patterns are very helpful to beginning readers because knowing these patterns helps them decode many new words. Also, they will decode words more efficiently when they are able to deal with larger chunks of letters. Use this assessment to learn which phonograms most of your children can already read, those they can almost read, and those they need to learn. Children who can read most of the words on these lists probably do not need to work on phonograms, although they may find it helpful to summarize their learning and sort words. You can also identify children who do not understand the concept of word patterns or have very little knowledge.

**How to Use It**
▶ Administer this test individually (use one of the included lists or prepare one of your own).
▶ If you are working with children near the beginning of first grade, you may want to begin with List 1, which includes very simple phonograms. If children are more advanced and you think that List 1 will be too easy, begin with List 2, which has the same phonograms with consonant clusters at the beginning.
▶ Check a child's reading of between ten and fifteen words at a time over several days. Note accurate responses with a ✓ and note substitutions, spelling nonword attempts phonetically.
▶ Use the Individual Record form to keep an ongoing record of each child's ability to read words with these regular phonogram patterns.

**What to Notice**
▶ Number of spelling patterns the child can recognize accurately
▶ Speed in recognizing patterns

Phonics & Word Analysis

# Phonogram Word Lists

| List 1 | List 2 | List 3 | List 4 |
|--------|--------|--------|--------|
| not | shot | ate | chore |
| man | slam | mane | pile |
| sit | twig | flake | dive |
| hen | when | bite | made |
| pan | drop | sing | smell |
| day | flap | flame | race |
| fat | slit | rag | stale |
| dog | sled | plane | cage |
| nap | bran | same | stage |
| tap | ship | drape | sale |
| pig | shut | plate | space |
| net | chin | drag | hive |
| tip | wet | bike | shade |
| red | plan | white | robe |
| nut | frog | strike | while |
| pin | spray | slime | poke |
| sad | that | tape | spell |
| rug | plug | bring | bore |
| hop | glad | rake | choke |
| jam | flip | dine | bell |

# Phonograms Assessment—**Individual Record**

Name _____  Grade _____

Directions: Ask the child to read each word. Check (✓) accurate responses and note substitutions.
Calculate the score for each list.

**List 1**

Date _____

| Word | ✓ |
|------|---|
| not | |
| man | |
| sit | |
| hen | |
| pan | |
| day | |
| fat | |
| dog | |
| nap | |
| tap | |
| pig | |
| net | |
| tip | |
| red | |
| nut | |
| pin | |
| sad | |
| rug | |
| hop | |
| jam | |
| **Score** | /20 |

**List 2**

Date _____

| Word | ✓ |
|------|---|
| shot | |
| slam | |
| twig | |
| when | |
| drop | |
| flap | |
| slit | |
| sled | |
| bran | |
| ship | |
| shut | |
| chin | |
| wet | |
| plan | |
| frog | |
| spray | |
| that | |
| plug | |
| glad | |
| flip | |
| **Score** | /20 |

**List 3**

Date _____

| Word | ✓ |
|------|---|
| ate | |
| mane | |
| flake | |
| bite | |
| sing | |
| flame | |
| rag | |
| plane | |
| same | |
| drape | |
| plate | |
| drag | |
| bike | |
| white | |
| strike | |
| slime | |
| tape | |
| bring | |
| rake | |
| dine | |
| **Score** | /20 |

**List 4**

Date _____

| Word | ✓ |
|------|---|
| chore | |
| pile | |
| dive | |
| made | |
| smell | |
| race | |
| stale | |
| cage | |
| stage | |
| sale | |
| space | |
| hive | |
| shade | |
| robe | |
| while | |
| poke | |
| spell | |
| bore | |
| choke | |
| bell | |
| **Score** | /20 |

Phonics & Word Analysis

## Phonograms Assessment—**Class Record**

| Name | Total score |
|---|---|
| 1. | |
| 2. | |
| 3. | |
| 4. | |
| 5. | |
| 6. | |
| 7. | |
| 8. | |
| 9. | |
| 10. | |
| 11. | |
| 12. | |
| 13. | |
| 14. | |
| 15. | |
| 16. | |
| 17. | |
| 18. | |
| 19. | |
| 20. | |
| 21. | |
| 22. | |
| 23. | |
| 24. | |
| 25. | |
| 26. | |
| 27. | |
| 28. | |

Notes

Phonics & Word Analysis

# Consonant Blends

**Description** Children read words, marking the consonant blends, or words with two or three consonant sounds together.

**You Need**
- Consonant Blends Word List
- Consonant Blends Assessment—Class Record form

**Why Use It** This assessment will provide information about the children's ability to recognize consonant blends within words and use that information to read words.

**How to Use It**
- Administer this assessment individually using the Consonant Blends Word List.
- Ask the child to read the list of words, going down each column.
- Score for accuracy and note substitutions.
- Use the Word List as the child's Individual Record form. Record the results on the Class Record form.
- For additional information, give the child a copy of the words, and ask him to highlight or circle all of the consonant blends he can find. Observe the speed and confidence he shows in finding consonant blends, as well as the accuracy. You can administer this task as a timed group assessment.

**What to Notice**
- Ability to use knowledge of consonant blends to read words
- Number of words with consonant blends the child can read
- Specific consonant blends the child controls in reading

Phonics & Word Analysis

# Consonant Blends Word List

Name _____  Date _____

Read the words and circle or highlight the consonant clusters in each one.

| | |
|---|---|
| spread | driving |
| dusk | float |
| train | creek |
| smooth | please |
| stream | frame |
| clever | splice |
| best | strike |

Phonics & Word Analysis

# Consonant Blends Assessment—**Class Record**

**Two-Letter Blends**

**Three-Letter Blends**

| Name | dusk | train | smooth | clever | float | creek | please | best | driving | frame | spread | stream | splice | strike |
|------|------|-------|--------|--------|-------|-------|--------|------|---------|-------|--------|--------|--------|--------|
| 1.   |      |       |        |        |       |       |        |      |         |       |        |        |        |        |
| 2.   |      |       |        |        |       |       |        |      |         |       |        |        |        |        |
| 3.   |      |       |        |        |       |       |        |      |         |       |        |        |        |        |
| 4.   |      |       |        |        |       |       |        |      |         |       |        |        |        |        |
| 5.   |      |       |        |        |       |       |        |      |         |       |        |        |        |        |
| 6.   |      |       |        |        |       |       |        |      |         |       |        |        |        |        |
| 7.   |      |       |        |        |       |       |        |      |         |       |        |        |        |        |
| 8.   |      |       |        |        |       |       |        |      |         |       |        |        |        |        |
| 9.   |      |       |        |        |       |       |        |      |         |       |        |        |        |        |
| 10.  |      |       |        |        |       |       |        |      |         |       |        |        |        |        |
| 11.  |      |       |        |        |       |       |        |      |         |       |        |        |        |        |
| 12.  |      |       |        |        |       |       |        |      |         |       |        |        |        |        |
| 13.  |      |       |        |        |       |       |        |      |         |       |        |        |        |        |
| 14.  |      |       |        |        |       |       |        |      |         |       |        |        |        |        |
| 15.  |      |       |        |        |       |       |        |      |         |       |        |        |        |        |
| 16.  |      |       |        |        |       |       |        |      |         |       |        |        |        |        |
| 17.  |      |       |        |        |       |       |        |      |         |       |        |        |        |        |
| 18.  |      |       |        |        |       |       |        |      |         |       |        |        |        |        |
| 19.  |      |       |        |        |       |       |        |      |         |       |        |        |        |        |
| 20.  |      |       |        |        |       |       |        |      |         |       |        |        |        |        |

Phonics & Word Analysis

# Vowel Clusters

**Description** Children read words with vowels that appear together and represent one sound.

**You Need**
▸ Vowel Clusters, Word Lists 1, 2, and 3
▸ Vowel Clusters Assessment—Individual Record form

**Why Use It** Children need to learn the various vowel combinations that often appear together in words. This knowledge will help them build the capacity to remember how words "look" rather than relying only on the sound. Knowing several examples for each vowel cluster will help children read new words.

**How to Use It**
▸ Begin by reviewing the list of words found on the Individual Record. Select the list that is most appropriate for your group of children. List 1 contains simple vowel combinations (*ee, ea, ai, oa*) that children may have learned in second grade. For an experienced group, you may want to begin with List 2, going on to List 3 if children find the tasks very easy.

▸ Have children read the list individually. Record their responses on the Individual Record by checking words read accurately and recording substitutions.

▸ It is not necessary for the child to produce 100% accuracy of all vowel combinations; consider the principle learned if there is a high level of accuracy. You will not need to provide a lesson on every vowel combination. If children know the principle and quite a few combinations, they will learn more from reading and writing.

**What to Notice**
▸ Number of words with vowel clusters the child can read
▸ Number of words with vowel clusters for which the child can provide accurate representation of the cluster
▸ Particular vowel clusters the child controls in reading

## Vowel Clusters, **Word List 1**

| | |
|---|---|
| seal | peel |
| sail | sweet |
| stain | heat |
| meal | braid |
| boat | lean |
| main | soap |
| real | train |
| rain | seen |
| speak | goat |
| sheets | neat |
| float | road |
| bean | |

Phonics & Word Analysis

## Vowel Clusters, **Word List 2**

| | |
|---|---|
| claw | grief |
| cows | grow |
| crawl | house |
| toe | moon |
| spoon | snow |
| new | pout |
| few | plow |
| good | spray |
| gray | thief |
| book | wood |

Vowel Clusters, **Word List 3**

| | |
|---|---|
| pour | hair |
| pearl | tier |
| boar | poor |
| air | rear |
| career | floor |
| your | peer |
| pier | soar |

Phonics & Word Analysis

# Vowel Clusters Assessment—**Individual Record**

Name _____ Age _____ Grade _____ Date _____

**List 1**

| Vowel Cluster | ✓ if the child shows good control of vowel cluster |
|---|---|
| seal | |
| sail | |
| stain | |
| meal | |
| boat | |
| main | |
| real | |
| rain | |
| speak | |
| sheets | |
| float | |
| bean | |
| peel | |
| sweet | |
| heat | |
| braid | |
| lean | |
| soap | |
| train | |
| seen | |
| goat | |
| neat | |
| road | |
| **Total** | |

| | | |
|---|---|---|
| **ee** | | |
| **ea** | | |
| **ai** | | |
| **oa** | | |

**List 2**

| Vowel Cluster | ✓ if the child shows good control of vowel cluster |
|---|---|
| claw | |
| cows | |
| crawl | |
| toe | |
| spoon | |
| new | |
| few | |
| good | |
| gray | |
| book | |
| grief | |
| grow | |
| house | |
| moon | |
| snow | |
| pout | |
| plow | |
| spray | |
| thief | |
| wood | |
| **Total** | |

| | | | | |
|---|---|---|---|---|
| **ay** | | **oo** | | |
| **aw** | | **ou** | | |
| **ew** | | **ow** | | |
| **ie** | | **oe** | | |

**List 3**

| Vowel Cluster | ✓ if the child shows good control of vowel cluster |
|---|---|
| pour | |
| pearl | |
| boar | |
| air | |
| career | |
| your | |
| pier | |
| hair | |
| tier | |
| poor | |
| rear | |
| floor | |
| peer | |
| soar | |
| **Total** | |

| | | | | |
|---|---|---|---|---|
| **eer** | | **ier** | | |
| **ear** | | **our** | | |
| **air** | | **oor** | | |
| **oar** | | | | |

## Vowel Clusters Assessment—**Class Record**

✓ if child accurately represented
the vowel cluster at least once

| Name | List 1 Easy | | | | List 2 More Difficult Vowel Clusters | | | | | | | | | List 3 Advanced *r*-Controlled | | | | | | | |
|---|---|---|---|---|---|---|---|---|---|---|---|---|---|---|---|---|---|---|---|---|---|
| | ee | ea | ai | oa | ay | aw | ew | ie | oo | ou | ow | oe | eer | ear | air | oar | ier | our | oor | | |
| 1. | | | | | | | | | | | | | | | | | | | | | |
| 2. | | | | | | | | | | | | | | | | | | | | | |
| 3. | | | | | | | | | | | | | | | | | | | | | |
| 4. | | | | | | | | | | | | | | | | | | | | | |
| 5. | | | | | | | | | | | | | | | | | | | | | |
| 6. | | | | | | | | | | | | | | | | | | | | | |
| 7. | | | | | | | | | | | | | | | | | | | | | |
| 8. | | | | | | | | | | | | | | | | | | | | | |
| 9. | | | | | | | | | | | | | | | | | | | | | |
| 10. | | | | | | | | | | | | | | | | | | | | | |
| 11. | | | | | | | | | | | | | | | | | | | | | |
| 12. | | | | | | | | | | | | | | | | | | | | | |
| 13. | | | | | | | | | | | | | | | | | | | | | |
| 14. | | | | | | | | | | | | | | | | | | | | | |
| 15. | | | | | | | | | | | | | | | | | | | | | |
| 16. | | | | | | | | | | | | | | | | | | | | | |
| 17. | | | | | | | | | | | | | | | | | | | | | |
| 18. | | | | | | | | | | | | | | | | | | | | | |
| 19. | | | | | | | | | | | | | | | | | | | | | |
| 20. | | | | | | | | | | | | | | | | | | | | | |
| 21. | | | | | | | | | | | | | | | | | | | | | |
| 22. | | | | | | | | | | | | | | | | | | | | | |
| 23. | | | | | | | | | | | | | | | | | | | | | |
| 24. | | | | | | | | | | | | | | | | | | | | | |
| 25. | | | | | | | | | | | | | | | | | | | | | |

Phonics & Word Analysis

# Suffixes

| | |
|---|---|
| **Description** | Children read words with suffixes that change the part of speech. |
| **You Need** | ▶ Words with Suffixes sheet |
| | ▶ Suffixes—Class Record form |
| **Why Use It** | This assessment will help you learn whether the children understand the concept that a suffix can change the part of speech and whether they can apply their knowledge of suffixes to read words. |
| **How to Use It** | ▶ Administer the assessment individually. |
| | ▶ Give the child a copy of the Words with Suffixes sheet. Say the base word (Column 1) for the child and then ask her to read the word with the suffix. |
| | ▶ As an alternative, use either the base word or the word with the suffix in a sentence and ask the child to circle the word you used. Demonstrate with the first sentence. |
| | ▶ Record the performance on the Class Record. Check the box if the student reads both words with the suffix correctly. |
| **What to Notice** | ▶ Number of words with suffixes the child can read |
| | ▶ Particular words and suffixes the child recognizes |
| | ▶ Speed with which the child reads words with suffixes |

## Words with Suffixes

Name _____ Date _____

| | | |
|---|---|---|
| **1.** | run | running |
| | | |
| **2.** | write | writer |
| | | |
| **3.** | work | worker |
| | | |
| **4.** | quick | quickly |
| | | |
| **5.** | sun | sunny |
| | | |
| **6.** | like | likely |
| | | |
| **7.** | high | highest |
| | | |
| **8.** | build | building |
| | | |
| **9.** | shine | shiny |
| | | |
| **10.** | bright | brightest |

Phonics & Word Analysis

# Suffixes—**Class Record**

| Name | -ing | -er | -ly | -y | -est |
|------|------|-----|-----|-----|------|
| 1. | | | | | |
| 2. | | | | | |
| 3. | | | | | |
| 4. | | | | | |
| 5 | | | | | |
| 6. | | | | | |
| 7. | | | | | |
| 8. | | | | | |
| 9 | | | | | |
| 10. | | | | | |
| 11. | | | | | |
| 12. | | | | | |
| 13. | | | | | |
| 14 | | | | | |
| 15. | | | | | |
| 16. | | | | | |
| 17. | | | | | |
| 18. | | | | | |
| 19. | | | | | |
| 20. | | | | | |
| 21. | | | | | |
| 22. | | | | | |
| 23. | | | | | |
| 24. | | | | | |
| 25. | | | | | |
| 26. | | | | | |
| 27. | | | | | |
| 28. | | | | | |

# Compound Words

**Description**  Children read simple compound words and identify the two words that have been put together.

**You Need**  ▶ Compound Words list

▶ Lined paper

▶ Markers and pencils

▶ Compound Words Assessment—Individual Record form

▶ Compound Words Assessment—Class Record form

**Why Use It**  This assessment will help you learn whether children can read simple compound words and identify the component parts.

**How to Use It**  ▶ Administer this assessment individually.

▶ Have the child read the 38 words on the Compound Words list. If the child finds a word difficult, prompt her once to look for a part she knows. On another copy of the form, note accurate responses and errors and score the number read correctly. Then ask the child to make a slash between the two component words.

**What to Notice**  ▶ Number of compound words the child recognizes

▶ Specific compound words the child recognizes

▶ Specific compound words the child can take apart

© 2008 by Irene C. Fountas and Gay Su Pinnell. Portsmouth, NH: Heinemann. This page may be photocopied.

Phonics & Word Analysis

## Compound Words

Name _____ Date _____

| | |
|---|---|
| airplane | grandmother |
| airport | haircut |
| anybody | headset |
| anything | himself |
| background | into |
| basketball | itself |
| bedroom | maybe |
| birdhouse | myself |
| birthday | nobody |
| cannot | playground |
| chalkboard | skateboard |
| cookbook | snowball |
| crosswalk | somebody |
| daytime | something |
| doorbell | sunshine |
| downstairs | today |
| earring | upset |
| everything | without |
| football | yourself |

# Compound Words Assessment—**Individual Record**

Name _____ Date _____

| Compound Words | | | |
|---|---|---|---|
| airplane | | grandmother | |
| airport | | haircut | |
| anybody | | headset | |
| anything | | himself | |
| background | | into | |
| basketball | | itself | |
| bedroom | | maybe | |
| birdhouse | | myself | |
| birthday | | nobody | |
| cannot | | playground | |
| chalkboard | | skateboard | |
| cookbook | | snowball | |
| crosswalk | | somebody | |
| daytime | | something | |
| doorbell | | sunshine | |
| downstairs | | today | |
| earring | | upset | |
| everything | | without | |
| football | | yourself | |
| | **/19** | | **/19** |

Phonics & Word Analysis

# Compound Words Assessment—**Class Record**

| Name | Number of accurate responses |
|---|---|
| 1. | |
| 2. | |
| 3. | |
| 4. | |
| 5. | |
| 6. | |
| 7. | |
| 8. | |
| 9. | |
| 10. | |
| 11. | |
| 12. | |
| 13. | |
| 14. | |
| 15. | |
| 16. | |
| 17. | |
| 18. | |
| 19. | |
| 20. | |
| 21. | |
| 22. | |
| 23. | |
| 24. | |
| 25. | |
| 26. | |
| 27. | |
| 28. | |

© 2008 by Irene C. Fountas and Gay Su Pinnell. Portsmouth, NH: Heinemann. This page may be photocopied.

# One- and Two-Syllable Words

**Description**     Children say a word, clap or tap a finger for each syllable, and then identify the number of syllables in the word.

**You Need**
▶ Word Cards

▶ Say and Sort Picture Cards

▶ Say and Sort Sheet

▶ One- and Two-Syllable Assessment—Individual Record form

▶ Syllable Assessments—Class Record form

**Why Use It**     These two assessments will give evidence as to whether children hear word parts and syllable breaks. Both tasks provide information as to whether children can hear and identify syllable breaks and say the number of syllables in each word. Use this information to form small groups of children who have difficulty hearing syllables and need more work. Task #1 is a simple clapping task. You can use the words suggested here or others that you add. Task #2 requires students to say and sort words by the number of syllables in the word.

**How to Use It**     **#1 Clap Syllables — Easy**     Administer this test individually. Prepare a list of ten one- and two-syllable words, for example: *hot, absent, paper, went, pumpkin, run, monster, find, water,* and *dream*. Be sure children have heard the words before and understand them. Ask children to clap the correct number of syllables. You can check whether each child's responses are accurate for each word.

**#2 Say and Sort — More Challenging**     Use the ten picture cards with one- and two-syllable words. Be sure children know the meaning of the words. Ask children to say each word and to sort them under the numerals (1 and 2). You can check whether each child's responses are accurate for each word. As an alternative, prepare a pencil-and-paper test in which children write the number of parts they hear next to each word.

**What to Notice**
▶ Number of words for which child can identify the correct number of syllables

▶ Ability to identify one- and two-syllable words

▶ Ability to represent sounds with letters

▶ Ability to represent syllables

# Say and Sort Picture Cards

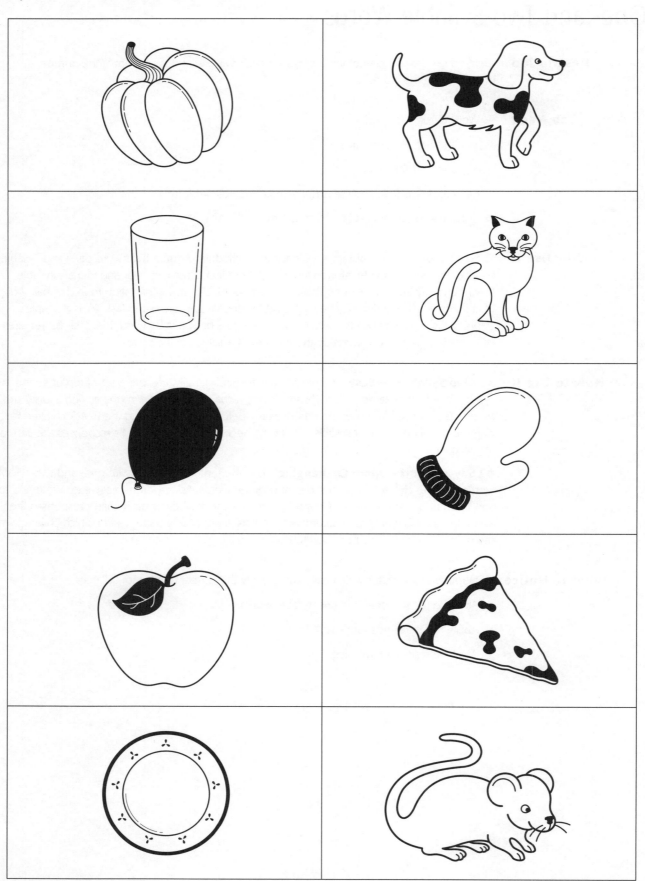

# Say and Sort Sheet

Name _____     Date _____

Glue the picture under the right number of syllables.

| 1 | 2 |
|---|---|
|   |   |

# One- and Two-Syllable Assessment—**Individual Record**

Name _____ Grade _____ Date _____

Directions: Ask the child to say the name of the picture on each card and sort the pictures onto the Say and Sort Sheet. Check if student identifies the syllables correctly.

| Words | Identifies number of syllables correctly |
|---|---|
| pumpkin | |
| glass | |
| balloon | |
| apple | |
| dish | |
| dog | |
| cat | |
| mitten | |
| pizza | |
| mouse | |

Notes

# Syllables in Longer Words

**Description**    Children demonstrate that they understand the concept of syllables, can hear syllable breaks, can count the number of syllables in a word, and have a beginning understanding of where to divide a word when hyphenating.

**You Need**
- ▶ Markers and pencils
- ▶ Syllables in Longer Words sheet
- ▶ Syllable Assessments—Class Record form

**Why Use It**    Most third-graders will be able to hear syllable breaks easily and count the number of syllables in a word. This ability to break words down into syllables is basic to word solving in both reading and writing. If you have already observed children's ability to hear syllables, you will not need to use this assessment. If some children do not seem to be breaking words down in this way, this quick assessment will help you identify those who need some small group work.

**How to Use It**
- ▶ Administer this assessment individually.
- ▶ Using the Syllables in Longer Words sheet, read each word aloud and have students say it softly to themselves. For each word, they place a line between syllables and circle the number of parts or syllables they hear.
- ▶ Use each student's sheet as an individual record. Do not be concerned about "correct" hyphenation, but notice children's use of their implicit sense of where the breaks would come in written words.
- ▶ If children correctly identify at least seven of the ten two-syllable words, place a ✓ by the child's name under "Identifies two syllables." Do the same for the ten three-syllable and four-syllable words.

**What to Notice**
- ▶ Number of words in which the child can hear and identify syllables
- ▶ Particular words children can read accurately
- ▶ Particular words that give children difficulty (for example, words with vowel pairs or consonant clusters)
- ▶ Ability to follow directions
- ▶ Speed with which children take words apart

Phonics & Word Analysis

# Syllables in Longer Words

Name _____ Date _____

Say the words. Mark the syllables with a slash. Circle the number of syllables you hear in each word.

| | | | | | | | | |
|---|---|---|---|---|---|---|---|---|
| 1. | absent | 1 2 3 4 | | 16. | independent | 1 2 3 4 | | |
| 2. | differences | 1 2 3 4 | | 17. | magnificent | 1 2 3 4 | | |
| 3. | calculator | 1 2 3 4 | | 18. | underneath | 1 2 3 4 | | |
| 4. | flavor | 1 2 3 4 | | 19. | monster | 1 2 3 4 | | |
| 5. | caravan | 1 2 3 4 | | 20. | tornado | 1 2 3 4 | | |
| 6. | excuse | 1 2 3 4 | | 21. | multiply | 1 2 3 4 | | |
| 7. | dessert | 1 2 3 4 | | 22. | water | 1 2 3 4 | | |
| 8. | wonderful | 1 2 3 4 | | 23. | plastic | 1 2 3 4 | | |
| 9. | different | 1 2 3 4 | | 24. | poisonous | 1 2 3 4 | | |
| 10. | inspect | 1 2 3 4 | | 25. | pretzel | 1 2 3 4 | | |
| 11. | habitat | 1 2 3 4 | | 26. | mysterious | 1 2 3 4 | | |
| 12. | conversation | 1 2 3 4 | | 27. | watermelon | 1 2 3 4 | | |
| 13. | interested | 1 2 3 4 | | 28. | demonstration | 1 2 3 4 | | |
| 14. | vacation | 1 2 3 4 | | 29. | stubborn | 1 2 3 4 | | |
| 15. | invention | 1 2 3 4 | | 30. | absolutely | 1 2 3 4 | | |

Phonics & Word Analysis

## Syllable Assessments—**Class Record**

Date _____

© 2008 by Irene C. Fountas and Gay Su Pinnell. Portsmouth, NH: Heinemann. This page may be photocopied.

| Name | Identifies one syllable | Identifies two syllables | Identifies three syllables | Identifies four syllables |
|---|---|---|---|---|
| 1. | | | | |
| 2. | | | | |
| 3. | | | | |
| 4. | | | | |
| 5. | | | | |
| 6. | | | | |
| 7. | | | | |
| 8. | | | | |
| 9. | | | | |
| 10. | | | | |
| 11. | | | | |
| 12. | | | | |
| 13. | | | | |
| 14. | | | | |
| 15. | | | | |
| 16. | | | | |
| 17. | | | | |
| 18. | | | | |
| 19. | | | | |
| 20. | | | | |
| 21. | | | | |
| 22. | | | | |
| 23. | | | | |
| 24. | | | | |
| 25. | | | | |
| 26. | | | | |
| 27. | | | | |
| 28. | | | | |

Phonics & Word Analysis

# Grade 1 Word Features Test

| | |
|---|---|
| **Description** | Children read 30 words, which include a variety of features. |
| **You Need** | ▶ Grade 1 Word Features List |
| | ▶ Grade 1 Word Features Test—Individual Record form |
| | ▶ Grade 1 Word Features Test—Class Record form |
| **Why Use It** | This assessment will give you information about which features of words children are able to attend to. The substitutions they make will also provide information about their knowledge of letter/sound relationships, spelling patterns, and word structure. |
| **How to Use It** | ▶ Administer this assessment individually. |
| | ▶ Ask the child to read the list of 30 words. |
| | ▶ On the Individual Record form, record the child's correct responses as well as substitutions. |
| **What to Notice** | ▶ Word features the child can read correctly |
| | ▶ Word features with which the child has difficulty |

## Grade 1 Word Features List

Read the words:

| | | |
|---|---|---|
| big | hole | she's |
| mat | ant | hammer |
| pet | Mom's | race |
| fun | puppy | jump |
| Kim's | seal | I'm |
| wave | bedroom | kiss |
| drop | boat | baseball |
| you'll | list | strip |
| feet | pile | bell |
| this | wash | white |

Phonics & Word Analysis

# Grade 1 Word Features Test—**Individual Record**

Name _____  Date _____

| Word | ✓ or substitution | Feature |
|------|-------------------|---------|
| big | | Consonant sounds (b, g); short vowel sound (i); simple phonogram patterns VC (ig) |
| mat | | Consonant sounds (m, t); short vowel sound (a); simple phonogram patterns VC (at) |
| pet | | Consonant sounds (p, t); short vowel sound (e); simple phonogram patterns VC (et) |
| fun | | Consonant sounds (f, n); short vowel sound (u); simple phonogram patterns VC (un) |
| Kim's | | Possessives |
| wave | | Phonogram patterns with a long vowel sound (VCe) |
| drop | | Consonant clusters (dr) |
| you'll | | Contractions (will) |
| feet | | Phonograms with double vowels (VVC) |
| this | | Consonant digraphs (th) |
| hole | | Phonogram patterns with a long vowel sound (VCe) |
| ant | | Short vowel sound (a) |
| Mom's | | Possessives |
| puppy | | Double consonants (middle); multisyllable words |
| seal | | Phonograms with two vowels (VVC) |
| bedroom | | Compound words; multisyllable words |
| boat | | Phonograms with two vowels (VVC) |
| list | | Consonant clusters (st) |
| pile | | Phonogram patterns with a long vowel sound (VCe) |
| wash | | Consonant digraphs (sh) |
| she's | | Contractions (is) |
| hammer | | Double consonants (middle); multisyllable words |
| race | | Phonogram patterns with a long vowel sound (VCe) |
| jump | | Consonant clusters (mp) |
| I'm | | Contractions (am) |
| kiss | | Double consonants (end) |
| baseball | | Compound words; multisyllable words |
| strip | | Consonant clusters (str) |
| bell | | Double consonants (end) |
| white | | Consonant digraphs (wh) |

# Grade 1 Word Features Test—**Class Record**

| | | | | | | | | | | | | | |
|---|---|---|---|---|---|---|---|---|---|---|---|---|---|
| big | | | | | | | | | | | | | |
| mat | | | | | | | | | | | | | |
| pet | | | | | | | | | | | | | |
| fun | | | | | | | | | | | | | |
| Kim's | | | | | | | | | | | | | |
| wave | | | | | | | | | | | | | |
| drop | | | | | | | | | | | | | |
| you'll | | | | | | | | | | | | | |
| feet | | | | | | | | | | | | | |
| this | | | | | | | | | | | | | |
| hole | | | | | | | | | | | | | |
| ant | | | | | | | | | | | | | |
| Mom's | | | | | | | | | | | | | |
| puppy | | | | | | | | | | | | | |
| seal | | | | | | | | | | | | | |
| bedroom | | | | | | | | | | | | | |
| boat | | | | | | | | | | | | | |
| list | | | | | | | | | | | | | |
| pile | | | | | | | | | | | | | |
| wash | | | | | | | | | | | | | |
| she's | | | | | | | | | | | | | |
| hammer | | | | | | | | | | | | | |
| race | | | | | | | | | | | | | |
| jump | | | | | | | | | | | | | |
| I'm | | | | | | | | | | | | | |
| kiss | | | | | | | | | | | | | |
| baseball | | | | | | | | | | | | | |
| strip | | | | | | | | | | | | | |
| bell | | | | | | | | | | | | | |
| white | | | | | | | | | | | | | |

Phonics & Word Analysis

# Grade 2 Word Features Test

**Description**   Children read 30 words, which include a variety of features.

**You Need**
▶ Grade 2 Word Features List

▶ Grade 2 Word Features Test—Individual Record form

▶ Grade 2 Word Features Test—Class Record form

**Why Use It**   This assessment will give you information about which features of words children are able to attend to. The substitutions they make will also provide information about their knowledge of letter/sound relationships, spelling patterns, and word structure.

**How to Use It**
▶ Administer this assessment individually.

▶ Ask the child to read down the list of 30 words.

▶ On the Individual Record form, record the child's correct responses as well as substitutions.

**What to Notice**
▶ Word features the child can read correctly

▶ Word features with which the child has difficulty

## Grade 2 Word Features List

Read the words:

| | | |
|---|---|---|
| Jack's | my | fish |
| need | loud | I've |
| tiger | remake | treat |
| knit | spy | replay |
| save | fast | know |
| I'll | comb | banana |
| umbrella | mule | scrap |
| hide | with | don't |
| lamb | we're | apple |
| dog's | baby | whale |

Phonics & Word Analysis

# Grade 2 Word Features Test—**Individual Record**

Name _____ Date _____

| Word | ✓ or substitution | Feature |
|---|---|---|
| Jack's | | Possessives |
| need | | Phonograms with double vowels (VVC) |
| tiger | | Multisyllable words, *r*-controlled vowel (er) |
| knit | | Silent consonants (k) |
| save | | Phonogram patterns with a long vowel sound (VCe) |
| I'll | | Contractions (will) |
| umbrella | | Multisyllable words |
| hide | | Phonogram patterns with a long vowel sound (VCe) |
| lamb | | Silent consonants (b) |
| dog's | | Possessives |
| my | | *Y* as a vowel sound |
| loud | | Phonograms with two vowels (VVC) |
| remake | | Prefixes (re); multisyllable words |
| spy | | *Y* as a vowel sound<br>Consonant clusters (sp) |
| fast | | Consonant clusters (st) |
| comb | | Silent consonants (b) |
| mule | | Phonogram patterns with a long vowel sound (VCe) |
| with | | Consonant digraphs (th) |
| we're | | Contractions (are) |
| baby | | *Y* as a vowel sound<br>Multisyllable words |
| fish | | Consonant digraphs (sh) |
| I've | | Contractions (have) |
| treat | | Phonograms with two vowels (VVC)<br>Consonant clusters (tr) |
| replay | | Prefixes (re) |
| know | | Silent consonants (k) |
| banana | | Multisyllable words |
| scrap | | Consonant clusters (scr) |
| don't | | Contractions (not) |
| apple | | Multisyllable words |
| whale | | Consonant digraphs (wh) |

Phonics & Word Analysis

## Grade 2 Word Features Test—**Class Record**

| | | | | | | | | | | | | |
|---|---|---|---|---|---|---|---|---|---|---|---|---|
| Jack's | | | | | | | | | | | | |
| need | | | | | | | | | | | | |
| tiger | | | | | | | | | | | | |
| knit | | | | | | | | | | | | |
| save | | | | | | | | | | | | |
| I'll | | | | | | | | | | | | |
| umbrella | | | | | | | | | | | | |
| hide | | | | | | | | | | | | |
| lamb | | | | | | | | | | | | |
| dog's | | | | | | | | | | | | |
| my | | | | | | | | | | | | |
| loud | | | | | | | | | | | | |
| remake | | | | | | | | | | | | |
| spy | | | | | | | | | | | | |
| fast | | | | | | | | | | | | |
| comb | | | | | | | | | | | | |
| mule | | | | | | | | | | | | |
| with | | | | | | | | | | | | |
| we're | | | | | | | | | | | | |
| baby | | | | | | | | | | | | |
| fish | | | | | | | | | | | | |
| I've | | | | | | | | | | | | |
| treat | | | | | | | | | | | | |
| replay | | | | | | | | | | | | |
| know | | | | | | | | | | | | |
| banana | | | | | | | | | | | | |
| scrap | | | | | | | | | | | | |
| don't | | | | | | | | | | | | |
| apple | | | | | | | | | | | | |
| whale | | | | | | | | | | | | |

Phonics & Word Analysis

# Grade 3 Word Features Test

| | |
|---|---|
| **Description** | Students read 30 words, which include a variety of features. |
| **You Need** | ▶ Grade 3 Word Features List |
| | ▶ Grade 3 Word Features Test—Individual Record form |
| | ▶ Grade 3 Word Features Test—Class Record form |
| **Why Use It** | This assessment will give you information about which features of words students are able to attend to. The substitutions they make will also provide information about their knowledge of letter/sound relationships, spelling patterns, and word structure. |
| **How to Use It** | ▶ Administer this assessment individually. |
| | ▶ Ask the student to read down the list of 30 words. |
| | ▶ On the Individual Record form, record the student's correct responses as well as substitutions. |
| **What to Notice** | ▶ Word features the student can read correctly |
| | ▶ Word features with which the student has difficulty |

## Grade 3 Word Features List

Read the words:

| | | |
|---|---|---|
| first | leave | waste |
| trouble | sunny | we've |
| bark | untie | remake |
| passing | homesick | rotten |
| chair | bird | boy |
| deer | batter | pie |
| they'd | corn | driveway |
| winter | rough | redo |
| noise | snore | beast |
| enter | you've | jellyfish |

Phonics & Word Analysis

# Grade 3 Word Features Test—**Individual Record**

Name _____ Date _____

| Word | ✓ or substitution | Feature |
|---|---|---|
| first | | Phonogram patterns in single-syllable words (VCCC) |
| trouble | | Syllable patterns in multisyllable words (ble) |
| bark | | Phonogram patterns in single-syllable words (vowels and r) |
| passing | | Syllable patterns in multisyllable words (VCC pattern, syllable juncture) |
| chair | | Consonant digraph (ch) |
| deer | | Phonogram patterns in single-syllable words (long vowel sound) |
| they'd | | Contractions (would) |
| winter | | Syllable patterns in multisyllable words (in) |
| noise | | Phonogram patterns in single-syllable words (/oy/) |
| enter | | Syllable patterns in multisyllable words (en) |
| leave | | Phonogram patterns in single-syllable words (VVCe) |
| sunny | | Syllable patterns in multisyllable words (un) |
| untie | | Prefixes (un) |
| homesick | | Compound words |
| bird | | Phonogram patterns in single-syllable words (vowels and r) |
| batter | | Syllable patterns in multisyllable words (at) |
| corn | | Phonogram patterns in single-syllable words (vowels and r) |
| rough | | Consonant digraph (gh) |
| snore | | Phonogram patterns in single-syllable words (long vowel sound) |
| you've | | Contractions (have) |
| waste | | Phonogram patterns in single-syllable words (VCCe) |
| we've | | Contractions (have) |
| remake | | Prefixes |
| rotten | | Syllable patterns in multisyllable words (VCC pattern, syllable juncture) |
| boy | | Phonogram patterns in single-syllable words (/oy/) |
| pie | | Phonogram patterns in single-syllable words (long vowel sound) |
| driveway | | Compound words |
| redo | | Prefixes (re) |
| beast | | Phonogram patterns in single-syllable words (VVCC) |
| jellyfish | | Compound words |

Phonics & Word Analysis

# Grade 3 Word Features Test—**Class Record**

| | | | | | | | | | | | | | |
|---|---|---|---|---|---|---|---|---|---|---|---|---|---|
| first | | | | | | | | | | | | | |
| trouble | | | | | | | | | | | | | |
| bark | | | | | | | | | | | | | |
| passing | | | | | | | | | | | | | |
| chair | | | | | | | | | | | | | |
| deer | | | | | | | | | | | | | |
| they'd | | | | | | | | | | | | | |
| winter | | | | | | | | | | | | | |
| noise | | | | | | | | | | | | | |
| enter | | | | | | | | | | | | | |
| leave | | | | | | | | | | | | | |
| sunny | | | | | | | | | | | | | |
| untie | | | | | | | | | | | | | |
| homesick | | | | | | | | | | | | | |
| bird | | | | | | | | | | | | | |
| batter | | | | | | | | | | | | | |
| corn | | | | | | | | | | | | | |
| rough | | | | | | | | | | | | | |
| snore | | | | | | | | | | | | | |
| you've | | | | | | | | | | | | | |
| waste | | | | | | | | | | | | | |
| we've | | | | | | | | | | | | | |
| remake | | | | | | | | | | | | | |
| rotten | | | | | | | | | | | | | |
| boy | | | | | | | | | | | | | |
| pie | | | | | | | | | | | | | |
| driveway | | | | | | | | | | | | | |
| redo | | | | | | | | | | | | | |
| beast | | | | | | | | | | | | | |
| jellyfish | | | | | | | | | | | | | |

Phonics & Word Analysis

# Vocabulary Assessments

In this section, you will find a rich array of assessments for identifying students' understanding of word meanings. Use this information in conjunction with the data you gather in the benchmark assessment conferences.

# Concept Words–**Number**

**Description**  Prompted by a picture card, children say the related concept word.

**You Need**
▶ Numeral and Number Word Cards sheet representing numbers one through twelve
▶ Dot Cards sheet
▶ Concept Words: Numbers and Colors—Class Record form

**Why Use It**  This assessment will give you information about children's oral vocabulary—that is, the extent to which they know the labels for number concepts. These words help young children read simple texts. Use this assessment to identify areas in which more instruction is needed and to determine which children need more support in developing their number vocabulary.

**How to Use It**
▶ Gather the three sets of cards: (1) cards with groupings of dots (one through twelve), (2) cards with the numerals 1 through 12, and (3) cards with the number words *one* through *twelve*. (If you think the concepts one through twelve are too difficult for most children, you can reduce the initial task to one through ten or one through five and administer the assessment again later in the year.)

▶ Select one or all of these options:
• Have children look at the cards with dots and tell you the appropriate quantity.
• Have children match the cards with dots and the numeral cards.
• Have children match the cards with dots and the number word cards.
• Have children read the numerals and words.
• Have children match the cards with dots, the numeral cards, and the number word cards.

▶ On the Class Record, write the number of correct items and note areas of confusion.

**What to Notice**
▶ Extent to which the child has developed a concept of number
▶ Ability to recognize and use number words
▶ Number of number words almost known

## Dot Cards

Vocabulary Assessments

## Numeral and Number Word Cards

| | | |
|---|---|---|
| 1 | 2 | 3 |
| 4 | 5 | 6 |
| 7 | 8 | 9 |
| 10 | 11 | 12 |
| one | two | three |
| four | five | six |
| seven | eight | nine |
| ten | eleven | twelve |

# Concept Words–**Color**

**Description**    Prompted by a picture card, children say the related concept word.

**You Need**
▷ Color Word Cards sheet

▷ For the colors *blue*, *yellow*, *orange*, *red*, *green*, *white*, *black*, and *purple*, prepare a set of cards depicting circles or squares in the appropriate color

▷ Concept Words: Numbers and Colors—Class Record form

▷ Matching Color Words sheet

**Why Use It**    This assessment will give you information about children's oral vocabulary—that is, the extent to which they know the labels for color concepts. These words help young children read simple texts. Use this assessment to identify areas in which more instruction is needed and to determine which children need more work in developing their knowledge of color words.

**How to Use It**
▷ Have children use the color and word cards to:
  • Say the appropriate color word for each color card.
  • Match the color cards and word cards or color boxes on the word cards with the appropriate color crayon (see the Color Words Matching sheet).
  • Read the word cards.

▷ Don't be concerned if you see children reading and matching the words printed on the crayons. If they can do this, the assessment is probably not necessary. Also remember that many boys have some degree of color blindness, and adjust your expectations accordingly.

▷ On the Class Record, write the number of correct items and note areas of confusion.

**What to Notice**
▷ Extent to which the child has developed a concept of color

▷ Ability to recognize and use color words

▷ Number of color words almost known

Vocabulary Assessments

## Color Word Cards

| | |
|---|---|
| red | green |
| yellow | blue |
| black | white |
| purple | orange |

## Matching Color Words

Name _____

Color the box.

blue

yellow

orange

red

green

white

black

purple

# Concept Words: Numbers and Colors—**Class Record**

Date _____

| Name | Number Words | | | | Color Words | | |
|---|---|---|---|---|---|---|---|
| | Matches Concept and Word Orally | Matches Concept and Numeral | Matches Concept and Word | Reads Numeral Word | Matches Concept and Word Orally | Matches Concept and Word | Reads Color Word |
| 1. | | | | | | | |
| 2. | | | | | | | |
| 3. | | | | | | | |
| 4. | | | | | | | |
| 5. | | | | | | | |
| 6. | | | | | | | |
| 7. | | | | | | | |
| 8. | | | | | | | |
| 9. | | | | | | | |
| 10. | | | | | | | |
| 11. | | | | | | | |
| 12. | | | | | | | |
| 13. | | | | | | | |
| 14. | | | | | | | |
| 15. | | | | | | | |
| 16. | | | | | | | |
| 17. | | | | | | | |
| 18. | | | | | | | |
| 19. | | | | | | | |
| 20. | | | | | | | |
| 21. | | | | | | | |
| 22. | | | | | | | |
| 23. | | | | | | | |
| 24. | | | | | | | |
| 25. | | | | | | | |
| 26. | | | | | | | |
| 27. | | | | | | | |
| 28. | | | | | | | |

# Concept Words in Isolation

**Description**   Children read and talk about a series of concept words: days of the week, seasons of the year, months of the year, weather words, position words (first, second, third, etc.).

**You Need**   ▶ Pocket chart

▶ Concept Word Cards sheet for days of the week, seasons of the year, months of the year, weather, and position or create your own (in enlarged version if used with pocket chart)

▶ Concept Words: In Isolation and in Sentences—Class Record form

**Why Use It**   These assessments will give you information about children's oral and reading vocabularies. It will help you notice the concept words that seem hard for individuals or the group in general to understand. You can use this information to plan future minilessons.

**How to Use It**   ▶ Administer these assessments individually, in a small group, or with the whole class.

▶ Assemble word cards for concept words that your students will be expected to know (days of the week, seasons of the year, months of the year, weather words, position words).

▶ Place word cards in the pocket chart. Ask children to try to read some of the words and then ask them what these words mean. After they respond, ask them or cue them as to the category of words, and then ask them to read the words again.

▶ Over time, accumulate results and enter them on the Class Record.

**What to Notice**   ▶ Slow responses

▶ Ability to recognize and use specific concept words

▶ Speed in recognizing words

Vocabulary Assessments

## Concept Word Cards

| | | |
|---|---|---|
| Sunday | Monday | Tuesday |
| Wednesday | Thursday | Friday |
| Saturday | January | February |
| March | April | May |
| June | July | August |
| September | October | November |
| December | winter | spring |
| summer | fall | sun |
| clouds | rain | snow |
| first | second | third |

# Concept Words in Sentences

**Description**    Children read sentences that include concept words (days of the week, seasons of the year, months of the year, weather words, etc.), locate the words, and then reread the sentences.

**You Need**
▶ Sentences that include concept words (select from sample set included or create your own based on children's experiences—Concept Word Sentences sheet)

▶ Concept Words: In Isolation and in Sentences—Class Record form

**Why Use It**    Many books that children read will feature these concept words. This assessment will give you information about children's ability to locate these words quickly and use them to monitor their reading.

**How to Use It**
▶ Administer this assessment to individuals or a small group; in a group, have children take turns.

▶ Prepare sets of sentences using concept words, and ask children to read them with you (Shared Reading). Examples of sentences are provided, but you will need to adjust them to fit your own environment.

▶ Then ask the children to locate specific concept words.

▶ Over time, accumulate results and enter them on the Class Record.

**What to Notice**
▶ The child's ability to locate specific concept words

▶ Number of concept words the child locates accurately

Vocabulary Assessments

# Concept Word Sentences

On Monday, I read a book.

On Sunday, I rode my bike.

On Saturday, I went to town.

On Friday, I had pizza.

On Thursday, I played with my friends.

On Wednesday, I went for a walk.

On Tuesday, I baked some cookies.

What did I do Monday?

What did I do Friday?

What did I do Tuesday?

---

Thirty days has September,

April, June, and November.

February has twenty-eight alone.

All the rest have thirty-one.

Excepting leap year, that's the time,

When February's days are twenty-nine.

What months are missing?

October is a month in the fall.

December means that winter is here.

January is the first month of the year.

In March the wind blows.

In May we know it is spring.

In July and August we go swimming.

There are twelve months in the year.

They are January, February, March, April, May, June, July, August, September, October, November, and December.

---

First, I wake up.

Second, I get out of bed.

Third, I brush my teeth.

Fourth, I get dressed.

Fifth, I eat breakfast.

Sixth, I put on my coat.

Seventh, I say good-bye to my dad.

Eighth, I get on the bus.

Ninth, I go to school.

Tenth, I say hi to my teacher.

What do I do second?

What do I do sixth?

What do I do tenth?

What do I do first?

What do I do fourth?

---

There are four seasons in the year,

summer, winter, fall [autumn], and spring.

What do you like to do in summer?

[children respond — make list]

What do you like to do in winter?

[children respond — make list]

What do you like to do in fall [autumn]?

[children respond — make list]

What do you like to do in spring?

[children respond — make list]

## Concept Words: In Isolation and in Sentences—**Class Record**

Date _____

| Name | Days | Months | Seasons | Position Words | Weather Words |
|------|------|--------|---------|----------------|---------------|
| 1. | | | | | |
| 2. | | | | | |
| 3. | | | | | |
| 4. | | | | | |
| 5. | | | | | |
| 6. | | | | | |
| 7. | | | | | |
| 8. | | | | | |
| 9. | | | | | |
| 10. | | | | | |
| 11. | | | | | |
| 12. | | | | | |
| 13. | | | | | |
| 14. | | | | | |
| 15. | | | | | |
| 16. | | | | | |
| 17. | | | | | |
| 18. | | | | | |
| 19. | | | | | |
| 20. | | | | | |
| 21. | | | | | |
| 22. | | | | | |
| 23. | | | | | |
| 24. | | | | | |
| 25. | | | | | |
| 26. | | | | | |
| 27. | | | | | |
| 28. | | | | | |

Vocabulary Assessments

# Concept Words

**Description**   Children read concept words and sort them into appropriate categories.

**You Need**
▶ Concept Word Lists (select from sample or create your own)

▶ Concept Words—Individual Record form

▶ Concept Words—Class Record form

**Why Use It**   You may want to check to see whether your students can read the concept words that they are generally expected to have learned in previous grades. Their ability to read this list will give you a quick check on this area of knowledge.

**How to Use It**
▶ Administer this assessment individually.

▶ Begin by reviewing the Concept Word Lists and choose lists appropriate for your children. Included are number words (*one* through *twenty-five*), harder color words, months of the year, weather words, position words (*first, second,* etc.). Some lists include words that are linked conceptually, for example, movement, weather, transportation, and time. These are groups of words that children meet frequently in the informational books they are beginning to read. You may want to look at the content curriculum for your district and identify concepts around which you can create a list of words.

▶ Select words that are appropriate. (Looking through books that children are expected to read will help.) You will probably not use all the words on any list.

▶ Have the student read each list of words and tell how they are alike.

▶ Note the results on the Individual Record. Space is provided for additional categories of concept words of your choosing. You can also record results on the Class Record.

▶ As an additional assessment, ask children to locate words in texts during guided, shared, or independent reading.

▶ You might also want to ask children to sort words into categories. Write the selected words on word cards, and have children sort in two or three categories.

**What to Notice**
▶ Ability to read specific words in categories

▶ Speed in recognizing words in a category

▶ Number of words known in each category

# Concept Word Lists

| Time words | Color words | Weather words | Transportation words |
|---|---|---|---|
| afternoon | aqua | breezy | airplane |
| AM | beige | brisk | automobile |
| annual | black | cloudy | boat |
| century | blue | cold | captain |
| daily | brick | cool | car |
| dawn | emerald | drizzle | crew |
| day | gold | fair | cruise |
| dusk | golden | hot | drive |
| evening | grape | lightning | driver |
| hour | gray | mild | engineer |
| minute | green | rain | ferry |
| monthly | lavender | showers | float |
| month | lime | snow | fly |
| morning | pink | storm | navigate |
| night | purple | sunny | passenger |
| PM | red | sultry | pilot |
| second | rose | thunder | railroad |
| sunrise | ruby | thunderstorm | railway |
| sunset | slate | tornado | sail |
| twilight | tan | warm | sedan |
| week | tomato | windy | ship |
| weekly | turquoise | | soar |
| year | violet | | steer |
| yearly | white | | train |
| | yellow | | |

Vocabulary Assessments

# Concept Word Lists

| Action words | Describing words that tell something about a person, place, or thing | Describing words that tell how or how much | Calendar words |
|---|---|---|---|
| come | beautiful | above | January |
| draw | big | around | February |
| go | dark | before | March |
| jump | flat | below | April |
| paint | hard | fast | May |
| read | light | happily | June |
| run | little | quickly | July |
| say | pretty | really | August |
| sprint | round | sadly | September |
| stand | short | slowly | October |
| walk | smooth | stubbornly | November |
| write | soft | very | December |
| | square | | day |
| | strong | | week |
| | weak | | month |
| | | | year |

# Concept Word Lists

| Motion words | Number words | Ordinal words |
|---|---|---|
| crawl | one | first |
| fly | two | second |
| dance | three | third |
| gallop | four | fourth |
| glide | five | fifth |
| hop | six | sixth |
| jump | seven | seventh |
| leap | eight | eighth |
| roll | nine | ninth |
| run | ten | tenth |
| saunter | eleven | eleventh |
| skate | twelve | twelfth |
| skip | thirteen | thirteenth |
| slide | fourteen | fourteenth |
| soar | fifteen | fifteenth |
| sprint | sixteen | sixteenth |
| stroll | seventeen | seventeenth |
| trot | eighteen | eighteenth |
| tumble | nineteen | nineteenth |
| walk | twenty | twentieth |
| | twenty-one | |
| | twenty-two | |
| | twenty-three | |
| | twenty-four | |
| | twenty-five | |

Vocabulary Assessments

# Concept Words—**Individual Record**

**Reading Category Words (Word Lists)**

| Category Word | Check ✓ If Read Accurately |
|---|---|
| Time words | /24 |
| Color words | /25 |
| Weather words | /21 |
| Transportation words | /24 |
| Action words | /12 |
| Describing words (List # _____) | /15 |
| Describing words (List # _____) | /12 |
| **TOTAL** | / |

**Reading Concept Words (Word Lists)**

| Content Area— Concept Words | Check ✓ If Read Accurately |
|---|---|
| Calendar words | /16 |
| Motion words | /20 |
| Number words | /25 |
| Ordinal words | /20 |
| **TOTAL** | / |

**Understanding Categories of Concept Words (Word Sorts)**

| Date | Type of Sort (categories) | Check ✓ if Successfully Sorted Words | Notes |
|---|---|---|---|
|  |  |  |  |
|  |  |  |  |
|  |  |  |  |
|  |  |  |  |

# Concept Words—**Class Record**

Directions: Check ✓ if student demonstrates an understanding of each set of concept words.

| Name | Time | Color | Weather | Transportation | Action | Describes Nouns | Describes How Much | Calendar | Motion | Number | Ordinal |
|------|------|-------|---------|----------------|--------|-----------------|--------------------|----------|--------|--------|---------|
|  |  |  |  |  |  |  |  |  |  |  |  |
|  |  |  |  |  |  |  |  |  |  |  |  |
|  |  |  |  |  |  |  |  |  |  |  |  |
|  |  |  |  |  |  |  |  |  |  |  |  |
|  |  |  |  |  |  |  |  |  |  |  |  |
|  |  |  |  |  |  |  |  |  |  |  |  |
|  |  |  |  |  |  |  |  |  |  |  |  |
|  |  |  |  |  |  |  |  |  |  |  |  |
|  |  |  |  |  |  |  |  |  |  |  |  |
|  |  |  |  |  |  |  |  |  |  |  |  |
|  |  |  |  |  |  |  |  |  |  |  |  |
|  |  |  |  |  |  |  |  |  |  |  |  |
|  |  |  |  |  |  |  |  |  |  |  |  |
|  |  |  |  |  |  |  |  |  |  |  |  |
|  |  |  |  |  |  |  |  |  |  |  |  |
|  |  |  |  |  |  |  |  |  |  |  |  |
|  |  |  |  |  |  |  |  |  |  |  |  |
|  |  |  |  |  |  |  |  |  |  |  |  |
|  |  |  |  |  |  |  |  |  |  |  |  |
|  |  |  |  |  |  |  |  |  |  |  |  |
|  |  |  |  |  |  |  |  |  |  |  |  |
|  |  |  |  |  |  |  |  |  |  |  |  |

# Synonyms I

**Description**  Children locate words that mean the same or about the same as words read by the teacher.

**You Need**
▶ Synonyms I Word Cards sheet

▶ Synonyms I Assessment—Class Record form

**Why Use It**  These quick oral assessments will help you know whether students understand the concept of synonyms in their listening and speaking vocabularies.

**How to Use It**
▶ Administer this assessment orally, either individually or with the whole class.

▶ Say the word pairs one after the other while you hold up the cards. If working with one child, ask her to clap when the two words mean the same or about the same. If working with the whole group, ask children to raise their hands when the two words mean the same or about the same.

▶ As an alternative, have children match pairs of synonym word cards.

▶ Enter the results on the Class Record.

**What to Notice**
▶ Number of word pairs a child can identify correctly

▶ A child's understanding of the concept of synonym

▶ The specific synonyms a child knows

## Synonyms I **Word Cards**

| | | |
|---|---|---|
| big | large | begin |
| start | close | shut |
| little | small | quit |
| stop | keep | save |
| call | yell | grab |
| take | jump | leap |
| ask | question | own |
| have | mean | cruel |
| happy | glad | below |
| under | end | finish |

Vocabulary Assessments

## Synonyms I Assessment—**Class Record**

Directions: Place a check mark in the box when the child correctly identifies the synonym.

| Name | big/large | begin/start | close/shut | little/small | quit/stop | keep/save | call/yell | grab/take | jump/leap | ask/question | own/have | mean/cruel | happy/glad | below/under | end/finish |
|---|---|---|---|---|---|---|---|---|---|---|---|---|---|---|---|
| | | | | | | | | | | | | | | | |
| | | | | | | | | | | | | | | | |
| | | | | | | | | | | | | | | | |
| | | | | | | | | | | | | | | | |
| | | | | | | | | | | | | | | | |
| | | | | | | | | | | | | | | | |
| | | | | | | | | | | | | | | | |
| | | | | | | | | | | | | | | | |
| | | | | | | | | | | | | | | | |
| | | | | | | | | | | | | | | | |
| | | | | | | | | | | | | | | | |
| | | | | | | | | | | | | | | | |
| | | | | | | | | | | | | | | | |
| | | | | | | | | | | | | | | | |
| | | | | | | | | | | | | | | | |
| | | | | | | | | | | | | | | | |
| | | | | | | | | | | | | | | | |
| | | | | | | | | | | | | | | | |
| | | | | | | | | | | | | | | | |
| | | | | | | | | | | | | | | | |
| | | | | | | | | | | | | | | | |
| | | | | | | | | | | | | | | | |
| | | | | | | | | | | | | | | | |
| | | | | | | | | | | | | | | | |
| | | | | | | | | | | | | | | | |
| | | | | | | | | | | | | | | | |
| | | | | | | | | | | | | | | | |

# Synonyms II

**Description**  Children read and identify words that mean the same or almost the same thing.

**You Need**  ▶ Synonyms II Word Cards sheet

▶ Synonyms II Assessment—Class Record form

**Why Use It**  This quick oral assessment will tell you whether the children understand the concept of synonym. Once this concept is understood, you can make a continuous list of synonyms, adding to it throughout the year, for children to refer to during word study, reading, and writing. Work with children who need help in small groups.

**How to Use It**  ▶ Administer this assessment individually or to the whole class. (Individually test children who do not seem to be responding successfully.)

▶ Hold up pairs of word cards, some that are synonyms and some that are not. Ask children to clap or raise their hands when the two words mean about the same. (Examples: *baby, infant; fix, mend; fetch, get; divide, split; near, close; quiet, silent.*)

▶ Enter the results on the Class Record form.

**What to Notice**  ▶ Child's understanding that there are words that can mean almost the same thing

▶ Number of words the child can read accurately

▶ Number of synonym pairs the child can form accurately

▶ Specific synonyms a child understands

Vocabulary Assessments

## Synonyms II **Word Cards**

| | | |
|---|---|---|
| baby | infant | back |
| rear | change | swap |
| city | town | divide |
| split | error | mistake |
| fetch | get | fix |
| mend | giant | huge |
| gift | present | pick |
| choose | messy | sloppy |
| near | close | quiet |
| silent | above | over |

*Fountas & Pinnell Benchmark Assessment System 1*

# Synonyms II Assessment—**Class Record**

Directions: Record the number of synonym pairs that each child correctly identified.

| Name | Score of correctly identified synonym pairs | Notes |
| --- | --- | --- |
| | /15 | |
| | /15 | |
| | /15 | |
| | /15 | |
| | /15 | |
| | /15 | |
| | /15 | |
| | /15 | |
| | /15 | |
| | /15 | |
| | /15 | |
| | /15 | |
| | /15 | |
| | /15 | |
| | /15 | |
| | /15 | |
| | /15 | |
| | /15 | |
| | /15 | |
| | /15 | |
| | /15 | |
| | /15 | |
| | /15 | |
| | /15 | |
| | /15 | |
| | /15 | |
| | /15 | |

Vocabulary Assessments

# Antonyms I

**Description**    Children read and identify words that mean the opposite or almost the opposite as words read by the teacher.

**You Need**
- Antonyms I Word Cards
- Antonyms I Assessment—Class Record form

**Why Use It**    These quick oral assessments will help you know whether students understand the concept of antonyms in their listening and speaking vocabularies.

**How to Use It**
- Administer this assessment orally, either individually or with the whole class.
- Say the word pairs one after the other while you hold up the cards. If working with one child, ask her to clap when the two words mean the opposite or almost the opposite. If working with the whole group, ask children to raise their hand when the two words mean the opposite or almost the opposite.
- As an alternative, have children match pairs of antonym word cards.
- Enter the results on the Class Record.

**What to Notice**
- Number of word pairs a child can identify correctly
- A child's understanding of the concept of antonym
- Specific antonyms a child knows

## Antonyms I **Word Cards**

| | | |
|---|---|---|
| on | off | up |
| down | in | out |
| long | short | buy |
| sell | hot | cold |
| low | high | big |
| little | open | close |
| asleep | awake | laugh |
| cry | old | young |
| stop | go | slow |
| fast | work | play |

Vocabulary Assessments

## Antonyms I Assessment—**Class Record**

Directions: Place a check mark in the box when the child correctly identifies the antonym.

| Names | on/off | up/down | in/out | long/short | buy/sell | hot/cold | low/high | big/little | open/close | asleep/awake | laugh/cry | old/young | stop/go | slow/fast | work/play |
|---|---|---|---|---|---|---|---|---|---|---|---|---|---|---|---|
| | | | | | | | | | | | | | | | |
| | | | | | | | | | | | | | | | |
| | | | | | | | | | | | | | | | |
| | | | | | | | | | | | | | | | |
| | | | | | | | | | | | | | | | |
| | | | | | | | | | | | | | | | |
| | | | | | | | | | | | | | | | |
| | | | | | | | | | | | | | | | |
| | | | | | | | | | | | | | | | |
| | | | | | | | | | | | | | | | |
| | | | | | | | | | | | | | | | |
| | | | | | | | | | | | | | | | |
| | | | | | | | | | | | | | | | |
| | | | | | | | | | | | | | | | |
| | | | | | | | | | | | | | | | |
| | | | | | | | | | | | | | | | |
| | | | | | | | | | | | | | | | |
| | | | | | | | | | | | | | | | |
| | | | | | | | | | | | | | | | |
| | | | | | | | | | | | | | | | |
| | | | | | | | | | | | | | | | |
| | | | | | | | | | | | | | | | |
| | | | | | | | | | | | | | | | |
| | | | | | | | | | | | | | | | |
| | | | | | | | | | | | | | | | |

# Antonyms II

**Description**     Children read and identify words that mean the opposite or almost the opposite.

**You Need**
▶ Antonyms II Word Cards sheet

▶ Antonyms II Assessment—Class Record form

**Why Use It**     This quick oral assessment will tell you whether children understand the concept of antonym. Once this concept is understood, you can make a continuous list of antonyms, adding to it throughout the year, for children to refer to during word study, reading, and writing. Work with children who need help in small groups.

**How to Use It**
▶ Administer this assessment individually or to the whole class. (Individually test children who do not seem to be responding successfully.)

▶ Hold up pairs of words, some that are antonyms and some that are not. Ask children to clap or raise their hands when the two words mean the opposite.

▶ Enter the results on the Class Record.

**What to Notice**
▶ Child's understanding that there are words that mean the opposite

▶ Number of words the child can read accurately

▶ Number of antonym pairs the child can form accurately

▶ Specific antonyms a child knows

© 2008 by Irene C. Fountas and Gay Su Pinnell. Portsmouth, NH: Heinemann. This page may be photocopied.

Vocabulary Assessments

## Antonyms II **Word Cards**

| | | |
|---|---|---|
| above | below | dark |
| light | dirty | clean |
| top | bottom | ask |
| tell | hard | soft |
| front | back | empty |
| full | heavy | light |
| enemy | friend | loose |
| tight | shallow | deep |
| rich | poor | push |
| pull | smooth | rough |

## Antonyms II Assessment—**Class Record**

Directions: Record the number of antonym pairs that each child correctly identified.

| Name | Score of correctly identified antonym pairs | Notes |
|---|---|---|
| | /15 | |
| | /15 | |
| | /15 | |
| | /15 | |
| | /15 | |
| | /15 | |
| | /15 | |
| | /15 | |
| | /15 | |
| | /15 | |
| | /15 | |
| | /15 | |
| | /15 | |
| | /15 | |
| | /15 | |
| | /15 | |
| | /15 | |
| | /15 | |
| | /15 | |
| | /15 | |
| | /15 | |
| | /15 | |
| | /15 | |
| | /15 | |
| | /15 | |
| | /15 | |
| | /15 | |
| | /15 | |

Vocabulary Assessments

# Homophones I

**Description**  Children listen to a sentence and circle the word (homophone) that has the right meaning in the sentence.

**You Need**
▶ Student Homophone Sheet
▶ Sentences with Homophones sheet
▶ Homophones I Assessment—Class Record form

**Why Use It**  Homophones can be very difficult for children. This assessment will help you identify those homophones they know and understand as well as those they do not know. Remember that children will continue learning about homophones and their use throughout elementary school; this assessment presents some of the easiest ones. Children will also be able to get the correct answers partly because they will notice that they can eliminate one of each pair once it is used. In other words, the answer to one homonym pair serves as a check on the other. Do not be concerned that this process makes the assessment too easy. You are gaining information about children's understanding of homophone pairs.

**How to Use It**
▶ Give this assessment to the whole class.
▶ Give children the Student Homophone Sheet and read over the list with them. You may want to divide this list into sets of 5–10 homophones rather than giving them all 27 at once.
▶ Remind children that these words sound the same but are spelled differently and have different meanings. You can tell which word to use by listening to the sentence and thinking about what the word means.
▶ Read one sentence to the children and have them circle the correct word. Then have them listen to the sentence with each item and circle the word.
▶ Keep the sheet as the child's individual record. Enter the results on the Class Record form.

**What to Notice**
▶ Number of homophones the child can use accurately
▶ Specific homophones the child can read and understand
▶ Understanding the concept of a homophone

## Student Homophone Sheet

Name _____ Date _____

Directions: Circle the word you hear in the sentence.

| | |
|---|---|
| 1. | to   two   too |
| 2. | to   two   too |
| 3. | to   two   too |
| 4. | be      bee |
| 5. | be      bee |
| 6. | their   there |
| 7. | their   there |
| 8. | I      eye |
| 9. | I      eye |
| 10. | blue   blew |
| 11. | blue   blew |
| 12. | our   hour |
| 13. | our   hour |
| 14. | dear   deer |

| | |
|---|---|
| 15. | dear   deer |
| 16. | ate   eight |
| 17. | ate   eight |
| 18. | your   you're |
| 19. | your   you're |
| 20. | no   know |
| 21. | no   know |
| 22. | read   red |
| 23. | read   red |
| 24. | see   sea |
| 25. | see   sea |
| 26. | one   won |
| 27. | one   won |

Vocabulary Assessments

## Sentences with Homophones

1. I want cookies, <u>too</u>.
2. The children have to go <u>to</u> school.
3. I have <u>two</u> trucks.
4. The <u>bee</u> landed on the flower.
5. Will you <u>be</u> my friend?
6. I want to go to <u>their</u> house.
7. Will she be <u>there</u> tomorrow?
8. <u>I</u> like to sing songs.
9. You can wink with your <u>eye</u>.
10. The sky is <u>blue</u>.
11. The wind <u>blew</u> the tree down.
12. We like <u>our</u> house.
13. We walked for an <u>hour</u>.
14. <u>Dear</u> friend, please come to my house.
15. I saw a <u>deer</u> leap across our yard.
16. I <u>ate</u> some french fries at the fair.
17. I saw <u>eight</u> birds fly by.
18. This is <u>your</u> book bag.
19. <u>You're</u> going to come with us, aren't you?
20. I <u>know</u> that boy.
21. <u>No</u>, don't do that.
22. I <u>read</u> two books yesterday.
23. I have new <u>red</u> sneakers.
24. I <u>see</u> the dog in the yard.
25. I sailed in a boat on the <u>sea</u>.
26. I have <u>one</u> sandwich.
27. She <u>won</u> the race.

# Homophones I Assessment—**Class Record**

Directions: Place a check mark in the box when the child correctly identifies the homophone.

| Names | to/too/two | be/bee | their/there | I/eye | blew/blue | our/hour | deer/dear | ate/eight | your/you're | no/know | read/red | see/sea | one/won | Total |
|---|---|---|---|---|---|---|---|---|---|---|---|---|---|---|
| | | | | | | | | | | | | | | |
| | | | | | | | | | | | | | | |
| | | | | | | | | | | | | | | |
| | | | | | | | | | | | | | | |
| | | | | | | | | | | | | | | |
| | | | | | | | | | | | | | | |
| | | | | | | | | | | | | | | |
| | | | | | | | | | | | | | | |
| | | | | | | | | | | | | | | |
| | | | | | | | | | | | | | | |
| | | | | | | | | | | | | | | |
| | | | | | | | | | | | | | | |
| | | | | | | | | | | | | | | |
| | | | | | | | | | | | | | | |
| | | | | | | | | | | | | | | |
| | | | | | | | | | | | | | | |
| | | | | | | | | | | | | | | |
| | | | | | | | | | | | | | | |
| | | | | | | | | | | | | | | |
| | | | | | | | | | | | | | | |
| | | | | | | | | | | | | | | |
| | | | | | | | | | | | | | | |
| | | | | | | | | | | | | | | |

Vocabulary Assessments

# Homophones II

**Description**    Children read a sentence and write the correct homophone in the blank space. They choose from two or three words.

**You Need**
▶ Homophones II Lists 1, 2, and 3

▶ Homophones II Assessment—Class Record form

**Why Use It**    Homophones are a challenge for many children, and confusions about them often persist into adulthood. This assessment will give you information about children's ability to use sentence context and meaning to choose the word that matches the meaning. Like adult spellers, children will be partially using a "process of elimination" strategy; that is, if they know one of the homophones, then it is easier to use it or eliminate it. You will have information about the extent to which children understand the principle that words can sound the same but be spelled differently and have different meanings. You can also identify homophones that are particularly difficult for many children, and you may want to address these in lessons.

**How to Use It**
▶ Administer this assessment individually or as a whole group.

▶ Using one of the Homophones II Lists provided, children read the sentence and think about which word will fit. They write the word in the blank space. If you have limited time, you may want children simply to circle the correct word. You may want to do a couple of examples with children so that they understand the task. You can also make the examples more accessible by reading down the list of homophones in the right columns so that children hear them before beginning the assessment.

▶ Record the results on the Class Record. Expect a fairly high score on this assessment to determine whether children understand the principle. (Remember that by guessing, children may still get many answers right.) If you can, observe children while they are working. You can note from their behavior whether they are simply guessing or carefully considering the meaning of the words.

**What to Notice**
▶ Number of homophones children correctly represent in sentence context

▶ Ease with which children perform the task

▶ Particular homophones that children can read and understand

▶ Particular homophones that children find difficult

# Homophones II **List 1**

Name _____ Date _____

Directions: Write the word in the sentence. Choose the correct one from the words on the right.

1. I _____ she would arrive late.

   new
   knew

2. When you make bread, you might use _____.

   flour
   flower

3. My _____ sent me a card for my birthday.

   ant
   aunt

4. Can you tell me the _____ to New York?

   way
   weigh

5. The girl shouted, "_____, guys!" to the boys.

   Hay
   Hey

6. I _____ my bike to my friend's house.

   road
   rode
   rowed

7. I ate the _____ salad.

   hole
   whole

8. This desk has nothing on it. It is _____.

   bear
   bare

9. Everyone is going to _____ at the new statue.

   stair
   stare

10. When you add the numbers you get the _____.

    some
    sum

Vocabulary Assessments

**11.** My grandmother taught me to _____.

sew
so

**12.** _____ going to be late for class.

Your
You're

**13.** I will _____ someone to help me with the work.

higher
hire

**14.** Speak loudly so I can _____ you.

hear
here

**15.** My mom is buying me _____ today.

close
clothes

**16.** My brother has a _____ named William.

son
sun

**17.** _____ you like to go to the movies tonight?

Wood
Would

**18.** They took _____ dogs for a nice long walk.

their
there

**19.** I saw a _____ hop over the rock.

hair
hare

**20.** _____ shirt do you like better?

Which
Witch

## Homophones II **List 2**

Name _____ Date _____

Directions: Write the word in the sentence. Choose the correct one from the words on the right.

© 2008 by Irene C. Fountas and Gay Su Pinnell. Portsmouth, NH: Heinemann. This page may be photocopied.

1. I lost the _____ of my left shoe.

   heal
   heel
   he'll

2. The weather had a big _____ on the game.

   affect
   effect

3. When you want to stop the car, put on the _____.

   break
   brake

4. The school _____ asked all the teachers to come to the meeting.

   principal
   principle

5. He _____ how to make model airplanes.

   knows
   nose

6. "I'm so tired," she _____.

   side
   sighed

7. In this game, you throw the _____ to move your marker.

   die
   dye

8. I hope I can _____ the earrings I lost.

   find
   fined

9. To make cookies, you must first make the _____.

   doe
   dough

10. The toy was on sale. It was _____.

    cheap
    cheep

Vocabulary Assessments

11. Would you like to _____ a new book to read?

    chews
    choose

12. He walked down the _____ at the grocery store.

    aisle
    I'll
    isle

13. The truck will _____ the trash away.

    hall
    haul

14. The postman dropped off the _____.

    male
    mail

15. I _____ a letter to my pen pal.

    cent
    sent
    scent

16. James was so _____ that he went to sleep.

    board
    bored

17. I like _____ pasta with sauce.

    plain
    plane

18. Do you _____ passing the potatoes?

    mind
    mined

19. My little sister _____ a cold.

    caught
    cot

20. The _____ for the bus is one dollar.

    fair
    fare

# Homophones II **List 3**

Name _____ Date _____

Directions: Write the word in the sentence. Choose the correct one from the words on the right.

1.  Everyone came to the game, _____ for Don, who was out of town.

    accept
    except

2.  During the storm, we saw some _____.

    hail
    hale

3.  Hannah _____ the answer to the question.

    guest
    guessed

4.  There is a _____ in the roof, and the rain is coming in.

    leak
    leek

5.  My old chair would _____ whenever I sat in it.

    creak
    creek

6.  On a cold morning, you can sometimes see _____ on the grass.

    dew
    due
    do

7.  There is a _____ of sheep on the hill.

    heard
    herd

8.  I told the plumber we need _____ to come right now.

    him
    hymn

9.  My voice is _____ from cheering at the concert.

    hoarse
    horse

10. The baker will _____ the dough to make the bread.

    knead
    need

Vocabulary Assessments

11. I _____ my bed every morning this week.

made
maid

12. I _____ want to have another slice of pizza.

might
mite

13. The storm forced the people to _____ to higher ground.

flea
flee

14. A chicken is a _____.

foul
fowl

15. You use the _____ to make a horse stop.

rain
reign
rein

16. When you wash something, you will want to _____ out the water.

ring
wring

17. It is very important to water the _____ of the plant.

root
route

18. The store was having a big _____.

sale
sail

19. The boys said that the game was not _____.

fare
fair

20. The choir sang a beautiful _____.

hymn
him

## Homophones II Assessment—**Class Record**

Directions: Record the number of homophones that each child correctly identified.

| Name | List 1 | List 2 | List 3 |
|---|---|---|---|
| | /20 | /20 | /20 |
| | /20 | /20 | /20 |
| | /20 | /20 | /20 |
| | /20 | /20 | /20 |
| | /20 | /20 | /20 |
| | /20 | /20 | /20 |
| | /20 | /20 | /20 |
| | /20 | /20 | /20 |
| | /20 | /20 | /20 |
| | /20 | /20 | /20 |
| | /20 | /20 | /20 |
| | /20 | /20 | /20 |
| | /20 | /20 | /20 |
| | /20 | /20 | /20 |
| | /20 | /20 | /20 |
| | /20 | /20 | /20 |
| | /20 | /20 | /20 |
| | /20 | /20 | /20 |
| | /20 | /20 | /20 |
| | /20 | /20 | /20 |
| | /20 | /20 | /20 |
| | /20 | /20 | /20 |
| | /20 | /20 | /20 |
| | /20 | /20 | /20 |
| | /20 | /20 | /20 |
| | /20 | /20 | /20 |
| | /20 | /20 | /20 |
| | /20 | /20 | /20 |

Vocabulary Assessments

# Vocabulary in Context

**Description**
Children use context to correctly identify the meaning of words from a Benchmark Assessment Book at their Instructional Level or Independent Level.

**You Need**
▶ The Benchmark Assessment Book at the child's Instructional Level or Independent Level.

▶ Assessing Vocabulary in Context—Individual Record form for the corresponding Benchmark Assessment Book.

**Why Use It**
As they read continuous text, readers constantly face vocabulary challenges. Many words they already know and can link to the array of letters that make up the word in print. Others may be new or only partially known. In this case, the reader derives the meaning from the context, and this ability is a key factor in comprehension. Often words have two or three alternative meanings. The reader must know precisely which definition is being used in a given text. This assessment will enable you to measure the student's knowledge of vocabulary as well as her ability to derive the precise meaning of words in the context of a short book.

**How to Use It**
▶ Choosing either the student's Instructional Level book or Independent Level book (or both), select words from the list on the corresponding Individual Record, checking those that you used.

▶ For each word, have the student turn to the page where the word appears. Then ask: "What does [word] mean in this book?"

▶ Score the student's answers using the following rubric:

| | |
|---|---|
| **0** | Did not respond or said "I don't know" |
| **1** | Made a response that is in some way related to the meaning of the word (any definition of that word) |
| **2** | Responded with a definition that is approximately the meaning of the word (same definition of the word as used in the text) |
| **3** | Responded with a full definition of the word (precise definition used in the text) |

▶ Using the chart below, determine whether the student's Vocabulary in Context score is Unsatisfactory, Satisfactory, or Excellent.

| Level | Unsatisfactory | Satisfactory | Excellent |
|---|---|---|---|
| A, B, C | 0–4 | 5–6 | 7–9 |
| D, E, F, G | 0–6 | 7–8 | 9–12 |
| H, I, J, K, L, M, N | 0–8 | 9–11 | 12–15 |

▶ Circle the rubric according to the total score.

**What to Notice**
▶ Number of words known or almost known

▶ Student's use of context to determine which meaning of a word is appropriate

Vocabulary Assessments

# Assessing Vocabulary in Context: Level A, Fiction
## Individual Record

Name _____  Grade _____  Date _____

### *Best Friends*

Check ✓ one:    Instructional Level: _____    Independent Level: _____

| Vocabulary Word (✓ 3 Words Selected) | | Meaning | Student Response |
|---|---|---|---|
| | dance, p. 4 | To move your body, usually to music | 0  1  2  3 |
| | climb, p. 8 | To move upward, often pulling with your hands to help you move | 0  1  2  3 |
| | slide, p. 10 | To move smoothly down the surface of a piece of playground equipment | 0  1  2  3 |
| | paint, p. 14 | To cover something with color | 0  1  2  3 |
| | | **Total Score** | |

**Score:**

**0**   Did not respond or said "I don't know"

**1**   Made a response that is in some way related to the meaning of the word (any definition of that word)

**2**   Responded with a definition that is approximately the meaning of the word (same definition of the word as used in the text)

**3**   Responded with a full definition of the word (precise definition used in the text)

| Level | Unsatisfactory | Satisfactory | Excellent |
|---|---|---|---|
| A, B, C | 0–4 | 5–6 | 7–9 |
| D, E, F, G | 0–6 | 7–8 | 9–12 |
| H, I, J, K, L, M, N | 0–8 | 9–11 | 12–15 |

▶ Circle the rubric according to the total score.

Vocabulary Assessments

# Assessing Vocabulary in Context: Level A, Nonfiction
## Individual Record

Name _____ Grade _____ Date _____

## *At the Park*

Check ✓ one:  Instructional Level: _____  Independent Level: _____

| Vocabulary Word (✓ 3 Words Selected) | | Meaning | Student Response |
|---|---|---|---|
| | catch, p. 6 | To get hold of something that is in the air | 0  1  2  3 |
| | jump, p. 8 | To launch yourself into the air | 0  1  2  3 |
| | swing, p. 10 | To move forward and backward while sitting on a hanging seat | 0  1  2  3 |
| | slide, p. 12 | To move smoothly down the surface of a piece of playground equipment | 0  1  2  3 |
| | | **Total Score** | |

**Score:**

**0**  Did not respond or said "I don't know"

**1**  Made a response that is in some way related to the meaning of the word (any definition of that word)

**2**  Responded with a definition that is approximately the meaning of the word (same definition of the word as used in the text)

**3**  Responded with a full definition of the word (precise definition used in the text)

| Level | Unsatisfactory | Satisfactory | Excellent |
|---|---|---|---|
| A, B, C | 0–4 | 5–6 | 7–9 |
| D, E, F, G | 0–6 | 7–8 | 9–12 |
| H, I, J, K, L, M, N | 0–8 | 9–11 | 12–15 |

▶ Circle the rubric according to the total score.

# Assessing Vocabulary in Context: Level B, Fiction
## Individual Record

Name _____ Grade _____ Date _____

### *My Little Dog*

Check ✓ one:     Instructional Level: _____ Independent Level: _____

| Vocabulary Word (✓ 3 Words Selected) | | Meaning | Student Response |
|---|---|---|---|
| | sleep, p. 2 | To rest your mind and body with your eyes closed | 0  1  2  3 |
| | eat, p. 4 | To take in food by chewing and swallowing it | 0  1  2  3 |
| | play, p. 8 | To take part in a game or activity, usually with others | 0  1  2  3 |
| | ride, p. 10 | To sit on or control something that moves | 0  1  2  3 |
| | read, p. 14 | To understand written words | 0  1  2  3 |
| | | **Total Score** | |

**Score:**

**0** Did not respond or said "I don't know"

**1** Made a response that is in some way related to the meaning of the word (any definition of that word)

**2** Responded with a definition that is approximately the meaning of the word (same definition of the word as used in the text)

**3** Responded with a full definition of the word (precise definition used in the text)

| Level | Unsatisfactory | Satisfactory | Excellent |
|---|---|---|---|
| A, B, C | 0–4 | 5–6 | 7–9 |
| D, E, F, G | 0–6 | 7–8 | 9–12 |
| H, I, J, K, L, M, N | 0–8 | 9–11 | 12–15 |

▶ Circle the rubric according to the total score.

Vocabulary Assessments

## Assessing Vocabulary in Context: Level B, Nonfiction
**Individual Record**

Name _____  Grade _____  Date _____

### Playing

Check ✓ one:   Instructional Level: _____  Independent Level: _____

| Vocabulary Word (✓ 3 Words Selected) | | Meaning | Student Response |
|---|---|---|---|
| | car, p. 4 | A vehicle with an engine and wheels that is used to move a small number of people from one place to another | 0  1  2  3 |
| | doll, p. 8 | A toy that is made to look like a person | 0  1  2  3 |
| | train, p. 10 | A vehicle with an engine that usually pulls a number of cars, runs on tracks, and carries people or things from one place to another | 0  1  2  3 |
| | plane, p. 12 | A vehicle that can fly and carries people or things from one place to another | 0  1  2  3 |
| | boat, p. 14 | A vehicle that floats in the water and carries people or things from one place to another | 0  1  2  3 |
| | | **Total Score** | |

**Score:**

**0**  Did not respond or said "I don't know"

**1**  Made a response that is in some way related to the meaning of the word (any definition of that word)

**2**  Responded with a definition that is approximately the meaning of the word (same definition of the word as used in the text)

**3**  Responded with a full definition of the word (precise definition used in the text)

| Level | Unsatisfactory | Satisfactory | Excellent |
|---|---|---|---|
| A, B, C | 0–4 | 5–6 | 7–9 |
| D, E, F, G | 0–6 | 7–8 | 9–12 |
| H, I, J, K, L, M, N | 0–8 | 9–11 | 12–15 |

▶ Circle the rubric according to the total score.

# Assessing Vocabulary in Context: Level C, Fiction
## Individual Record

Name _____ Grade _____ Date _____

### Socks

Check ✓ one:    Instructional Level: _____    Independent Level: _____

| Vocabulary Word (✓ 3 Words Selected) | | Meaning | Student Response |
|---|---|---|---|
| | wake, p. 2 | To stop sleeping | 0  1  2  3 |
| | couch, p. 6 | A piece of furniture that you can sit or lie on | 0  1  2  3 |
| | window, p. 10 | An opening in a wall that lets in light and air | 0  1  2  3 |
| | under, p. 14 | Below or beneath | 0  1  2  3 |
| | | **Total Score** | |

**Score:**

**0**  Did not respond or said "I don't know"

**1**  Made a response that is in some way related to the meaning of the word (any definition of that word)

**2**  Responded with a definition that is approximately the meaning of the word (same definition of the word as used in the text)

**3**  Responded with a full definition of the word (precise definition used in the text)

| Level | Unsatisfactory | Satisfactory | Excellent |
|---|---|---|---|
| A, B, C | 0–4 | 5–6 | 7–9 |
| D, E, F, G | 0–6 | 7–8 | 9–12 |
| H, I, J, K, L, M, N | 0–8 | 9–11 | 12–15 |

▶ Circle the rubric according to the total score.

Vocabulary Assessments

# Assessing Vocabulary in Context: Level C, Nonfiction
## Individual Record

Name _____ Grade _____ Date _____

## *Shopping*

Check ✓ one: Instructional Level: _____ Independent Level: _____

| Vocabulary Word (✓ 3 Words Selected) | | Meaning | Student Response |
|---|---|---|---|
| | apples, p. 4 | A red fruit with a thin skin that can be eaten | 0 1 2 3 |
| | oranges, p. 8 | A fruit with a thick skin that must be peeled off before eating the inside | 0 1 2 3 |
| | bread, p. 14 | A food made with flour and other ingredients and baked in an oven; it is often cut into slices | 0 1 2 3 |
| | cookies, p. 16 | Small, sweet-tasting cakes | 0 1 2 3 |
| | | **Total Score** | |

**Score:**

**0** Did not respond or said "I don't know"

**1** Made a response that is in some way related to the meaning of the word (any definition of that word)

**2** Responded with a definition that is approximately the meaning of the word (same definition of the word as used in the text)

**3** Responded with a full definition of the word (precise definition used in the text)

| Level | Unsatisfactory | Satisfactory | Excellent |
|---|---|---|---|
| A, B, C | 0–4 | 5–6 | 7–9 |
| D, E, F, G | 0–6 | 7–8 | 9–12 |
| H, I, J, K, L, M, N | 0–8 | 9–11 | 12–15 |

▶ Circle the rubric according to the total score.

Vocabulary Assessments

# Assessing Vocabulary in Context: Level D, Fiction
## Individual Record

Name _____  Grade _____  Date _____

### *The Nice Little House*

Check ✓ one:  Instructional Level: _____  Independent Level: _____

| Vocabulary Word (✓ 4 Words Selected) | | Meaning | Student Response |
|---|---|---|---|
| | horse, p. 2 | A large animal that is often used to pull things or to ride on | 0  1  2  3 |
| | little, p. 2 | Small in size | 0  1  2  3 |
| | nice, p. 2 | Pleasant or good | 0  1  2  3 |
| | chicken, p. 8 | A kind of bird, often used to lay eggs for humans to eat | 0  1  2  3 |
| | duck, p. 10 | A water bird with a wide, flat beak (called a bill) and webbed feet | 0  1  2  3 |
| | skunk, p. 12 | A bad-smelling animal with black and white fur | 0  1  2  3 |
| | | **Total Score** | |

**Score:**

**0**  Did not respond or said "I don't know"

**1**  Made a response that is in some way related to the meaning of the word (any definition of that word)

**2**  Responded with a definition that is approximately the meaning of the word (same definition of the word as used in the text)

**3**  Responded with a full definition of the word (precise definition used in the text)

| Level | Unsatisfactory | Satisfactory | Excellent |
|---|---|---|---|
| A, B, C | 0–4 | 5–6 | 7–9 |
| D, E, F, G | 0–6 | 7–8 | 9–12 |
| H, I, J, K, L, M, N | 0–8 | 9–11 | 12–15 |

▶ Circle the rubric according to the total score.

Vocabulary Assessments

# Assessing Vocabulary in Context: Level D, Nonfiction
## Individual Record

Name _____  Grade _____  Date _____

### *Our Teacher Mr. Brown*

Check ✓ one:  Instructional Level: _____  Independent Level: _____

| Vocabulary Word (✓ 4 Words Selected) | | Meaning | Student Response |
|---|---|---|---|
| | teacher, p. 2 | A person who helps others learn about things | 0  1  2  3 |
| | write, p. 6 | To make letters or words | 0  1  2  3 |
| | read, p. 6 | To say written words aloud | 0  1  2  3 |
| | books, p. 8 | Pages with words on them, collected together with a cover | 0  1  2  3 |
| | paint, p. 10 | To cover a surface with colorful liquid | 0  1  2  3 |
| | draw, p. 10 | To make a picture of something with a pen, a pencil, or any writing tool | 0  1  2  3 |
| | | **Total Score** | |

**Score:**

**0**  Did not respond or said "I don't know"

**1**  Made a response that is in some way related to the meaning of the word (any definition of that word)

**2**  Responded with a definition that is approximately the meaning of the word (same definition of the word as used in the text)

**3**  Responded with a full definition of the word (precise definition used in the text)

| Level | Unsatisfactory | Satisfactory | Excellent |
|---|---|---|---|
| A, B, C | 0–4 | 5–6 | 7–9 |
| D, E, F, G | 0–6 | 7–8 | 9–12 |
| H, I, J, K, L, M, N | 0–8 | 9–11 | 12–15 |

▶ Circle the rubric according to the total score.

# Assessing Vocabulary in Context: Level E, Fiction
## Individual Record

Name _____  Grade _____  Date _____

### *The Loose Tooth*

Check ✓ one:    Instructional Level: _____    Independent Level: _____

| Vocabulary Word (✓ 4 Words Selected) | | Meaning | Student Response |
|---|---|---|---|
| | loose, p. 2 | Not held in place well; not tight | 0 1 2 3 |
| | very, p. 2 | Extremely; to a large degree; a lot | 0 1 2 3 |
| | breakfast, p. 4 | The first meal of the day, eaten in the morning | 0 1 2 3 |
| | wiggled, p. 5 | Moved back and forth | 0 1 2 3 |
| | lunch, p. 10 | The meal eaten in the middle of the day | 0 1 2 3 |
| | soup, p. 13 | A liquid food, usually with vegetables or meats in it | 0 1 2 3 |
| | bite, p. 15 | A piece of food that is taken by the mouth from a larger piece of food | 0 1 2 3 |
| | | **Total Score** | |

**Score:**

**0**  Did not respond or said "I don't know"

**1**  Made a response that is in some way related to the meaning of the word (any definition of that word)

**2**  Responded with a definition that is approximately the meaning of the word (same definition of the word as used in the text)

**3**  Responded with a full definition of the word (precise definition used in the text)

| Level | Unsatisfactory | Satisfactory | Excellent |
|---|---|---|---|
| A, B, C | 0–4 | 5–6 | 7–9 |
| D, E, F, G | 0–6 | 7–8 | 9–12 |
| H, I, J, K, L, M, N | 0–8 | 9–11 | 12–15 |

▶ Circle the rubric according to the total score.

Vocabulary Assessments

## Assessing Vocabulary in Context: Level E, Nonfiction
**Individual Record**

Name _____ Grade _____ Date _____

### The Zoo

Check ✓ one:    Instructional Level: _____    Independent Level: _____

| Vocabulary Word (✓ 4 Words Selected) | | Meaning | Student Response |
|---|---|---|---|
| | elephant, p. 2 | A very large animal with big ears and a trunk | 0  1  2  3 |
| | polar bears, p. 6 | Large, white animals that live in very cold places | 0  1  2  3 |
| | fur, p. 6 | A soft, hairy covering that some animals have on their bodies | 0  1  2  3 |
| | lions, p. 8 | Large animals that belong to the cat family | 0  1  2  3 |
| | giraffes, p. 10 | Animals with very long necks | 0  1  2  3 |
| | penguins, p. 12 | Black and white birds that live in cold places and cannot fly | 0  1  2  3 |
| | chimps, p. 14 | Animals that live in forests and are related to apes | 0  1  2  3 |
| | | **Total Score** | |

**Score:**

**0**   Did not respond or said "I don't know"

**1**   Made a response that is in some way related to the meaning of the word (any definition of that word)

**2**   Responded with a definition that is approximately the meaning of the word (same definition of the word as used in the text)

**3**   Responded with a full definition of the word (precise definition used in the text)

| Level | Unsatisfactory | Satisfactory | Excellent |
|---|---|---|---|
| A, B, C | 0–4 | 5–6 | 7–9 |
| D, E, F, G | 0–6 | 7–8 | 9–12 |
| H, I, J, K, L, M, N | 0–8 | 9–11 | 12–15 |

▶ Circle the rubric according to the total score.

## Assessing Vocabulary in Context: Level F, Fiction
# Individual Record

Name _____ Grade _____ Date _____

### *Anna's New Glasses*

Check ✓ one:   Instructional Level: _____   Independent Level: _____

| Vocabulary Word (✓ 4 Words Selected) | | Meaning | Student Response |
|---|---|---|---|
| | ready, p. 2 | Able to start; prepared | 0 1 2 3 |
| | school, p. 2 | A place where people go to learn | 0 1 2 3 |
| | backpack, p. 2 | A bag worn on the back, with straps that go on the shoulders | 0 1 2 3 |
| | glasses, p. 2 | A frame with lenses, worn on the face to help someone see better | 0 1 2 3 |
| | doctor, p. 6 | A person who is trained to help sick or injured people get better | 0 1 2 3 |
| | great, p. 11 | Good; special | 0 1 2 3 |
| | | **Total Score** | |

**Score:**

**0** Did not respond or said "I don't know"

**1** Made a response that is in some way related to the meaning of the word (any definition of that word)

**2** Responded with a definition that is approximately the meaning of the word (same definition of the word as used in the text)

**3** Responded with a full definition of the word (precise definition used in the text)

| Level | Unsatisfactory | Satisfactory | Excellent |
|---|---|---|---|
| A, B, C | 0–4 | 5–6 | 7–9 |
| D, E, F, G | 0–6 | 7–8 | 9–12 |
| H, I, J, K, L, M, N | 0–8 | 9–11 | 12–15 |

▶ Circle the rubric according to the total score.

# Assessing Vocabulary in Context: Level F, Nonfiction
## Individual Record

Name _____ Grade _____ Date _____

### *From Nest to Bird*

Check ✓ one:   Instructional Level: _____   Independent Level: _____

| Vocabulary Word (✓ 4 Words Selected) | | Meaning | Student Response |
|---|---|---|---|
| | sticks, p. 3 | Small branches broken off from trees | 0  1  2  3 |
| | grass, p. 3 | Plants with long, skinny leaves | 0  1  2  3 |
| | nest, p. 3 | Something a bird makes to keep its eggs safe and warm | 0  1  2  3 |
| | eggs, p. 5 | Round objects produced by some female animals that have a baby animal inside | 0  1  2  3 |
| | warm, p. 7 | A temperature between cold and hot | 0  1  2  3 |
| | bugs, p. 11 | Small animals that creep and crawl; insects | 0  1  2  3 |
| | | **Total Score** | |

**Score:**

**0**  Did not respond or said "I don't know"

**1**  Made a response that is in some way related to the meaning of the word (any definition of that word)

**2**  Responded with a definition that is approximately the meaning of the word (same definition of the word as used in the text)

**3**  Responded with a full definition of the word (precise definition used in the text)

| Level | Unsatisfactory | Satisfactory | Excellent |
|---|---|---|---|
| A, B, C | 0–4 | 5–6 | 7–9 |
| D, E, F, G | 0–6 | 7–8 | 9–12 |
| H, I, J, K, L, M, N | 0–8 | 9–11 | 12–15 |

▶ Circle the rubric according to the total score.

# Assessing Vocabulary in Context: Level G, Fiction
## Individual Record

Name _____  Grade _____  Date _____

### *Bedtime for Nick*

Check ✓ one:  Instructional Level: _____  Independent Level: _____

| Vocabulary Word<br>(✓ 4 Words Selected) | | Meaning | Student Response |
|---|---|---|---|
| | pajamas, p. 4 | Clothes worn to bed | 0  1  2  3 |
| | washed, p. 4 | Cleaned, with soap and water | 0  1  2  3 |
| | brushed, p. 4 | Scrubbed in order to clean | 0  1  2  3 |
| | over, p. 6 | Finished; done; completed | 0  1  2  3 |
| | nightlight, p. 8 | A small light that is left on at night when other lights are turned off | 0  1  2  3 |
| | open, p. 12 | To change from a shut or closed position | 0  1  2  3 |
| | missing, p. 14 | Absent; not present; lost | 0  1  2  3 |
| | | **Total Score** | |

**Score:**

**0**  Did not respond or said "I don't know"

**1**  Made a response that is in some way related to the meaning of the word (any definition of that word)

**2**  Responded with a definition that is approximately the meaning of the word (same definition of the word as used in the text)

**3**  Responded with a full definition of the word (precise definition used in the text)

| Level | Unsatisfactory | Satisfactory | Excellent |
|---|---|---|---|
| A, B, C | 0–4 | 5–6 | 7–9 |
| D, E, F, G | 0–6 | 7–8 | 9–12 |
| H, I, J, K, L, M, N | 0–8 | 9–11 | 12–15 |

▶ Circle the rubric according to the total score.

Vocabulary Assessments

# Assessing Vocabulary in Context: Level G, Nonfiction
## Individual Record

Name _____   Grade _____   Date _____

## Bubbles

Check ✓ one:     Instructional Level: _____     Independent Level: _____

| Vocabulary Word (✓ 4 Words Selected) | | Meaning | Student Response |
|---|---|---|---|
| | shiny, p. 4 | Bright; giving off light | 0  1  2  3 |
| | rainbow, p. 4 | An arc of colors | 0  1  2  3 |
| | inside, p. 6 | In the interior of | 0  1  2  3 |
| | filled, p. 6 | Full of | 0  1  2  3 |
| | air, p. 6 | The invisible gases that are all around us | 0  1  2  3 |
| | blowing, p. 9 | Pushing out a stream of air from the mouth | 0  1  2  3 |
| | enormous, p. 12 | Very large | 0  1  2  3 |
| | pop, p. 16 | To burst with a sharp sound | 0  1  2  3 |
| | | **Total Score** | |

**Score:**

**0**   Did not respond or said "I don't know"

**1**   Made a response that is in some way related to the meaning of the word (any definition of that word)

**2**   Responded with a definition that is approximately the meaning of the word (same definition of the word as used in the text)

**3**   Responded with a full definition of the word (precise definition used in the text)

| Level | Unsatisfactory | Satisfactory | Excellent |
|---|---|---|---|
| A, B, C | 0–4 | 5–6 | 7–9 |
| D, E, F, G | 0–6 | 7–8 | 9–12 |
| H, I, J, K, L, M, N | 0–8 | 9–11 | 12–15 |

▶ Circle the rubric according to the total score.

# Assessing Vocabulary in Context: Level H, Fiction
## Individual Record

Name _____ Grade _____ Date _____

### *The Sleepover Party*

Check ✓ one:  Instructional Level: _____ Independent Level: _____

| Vocabulary Word (✓ 5 Words Selected) | | Meaning | Student Response |
|---|---|---|---|
| | worried, p. 2 | Concerned; thinking something bad might happen | 0  1  2  3 |
| | invited, p. 3 | Asked to attend | 0  1  2  3 |
| | pack, p. 4 | To put things into a container | 0  1  2  3 |
| | listening, p. 5 | Paying attention to what someone is saying | 0  1  2  3 |
| | thought, p. 5 | Had an idea in the mind | 0  1  2  3 |
| | favorite, p. 6 | Something that is favored or preferred over all others | 0  1  2  3 |
| | answered, p. 9 | Replied; responded | 0  1  2  3 |
| | still, p. 9 | Continuing to be; in the same state as a previous time | 0  1  2  3 |
| | | **Total Score** | |

**Score:**

**0**  Did not respond or said "I don't know"

**1**  Made a response that is in some way related to the meaning of the word (any definition of that word)

**2**  Responded with a definition that is approximately the meaning of the word (same definition of the word as used in the text)

**3**  Responded with a full definition of the word (precise definition used in the text)

| Level | Unsatisfactory | Satisfactory | Excellent |
|---|---|---|---|
| A, B, C | 0–4 | 5–6 | 7–9 |
| D, E, F, G | 0–6 | 7–8 | 9–12 |
| H, I, J, K, L, M, N | 0–8 | 9–11 | 12–15 |

▶ Circle the rubric according to the total score.

Vocabulary Assessments

# Assessing Vocabulary in Context: Level H, Nonfiction
## Individual Record

Name _____  Grade _____  Date _____

## *Trucks*

Check ✓ one:    Instructional Level: _____    Independent Level: _____

| Vocabulary Word (✓ 5 Words Selected) | | Meaning | Student Response |
|---|---|---|---|
| | truck, p. 4 | A vehicle for carrying large, heavy things | 0  1  2  3 |
| | hose, p. 4 | A bendable tube that carries liquid from one place to another | 0  1  2  3 |
| | trash, p. 6 | Waste; unwanted, leftover items | 0  1  2  3 |
| | crushes, p. 6 | Squeezes; flattens | 0  1  2  3 |
| | carries, p. 6 | Brings from one place to another; transports | 0  1  2  3 |
| | snowplow, p. 10 | A device used to push or carry away snow | 0  1  2  3 |
| | market, p. 12 | A place where things are bought and sold | 0  1  2  3 |
| | work, p. 16 | Job; something that needs to be done | 0  1  2  3 |
| | | **Total Score** | |

**Score:**

**0** Did not respond or said "I don't know"

**1** Made a response that is in some way related to the meaning of the word (any definition of that word)

**2** Responded with a definition that is approximately the meaning of the word (same definition of the word as used in the text)

**3** Responded with a full definition of the word (precise definition used in the text)

| Level | Unsatisfactory | Satisfactory | Excellent |
|---|---|---|---|
| A, B, C | 0–4 | 5–6 | 7–9 |
| D, E, F, G | 0–6 | 7–8 | 9–12 |
| H, I, J, K, L, M, N | 0–8 | 9–11 | 12–15 |

▶ Circle the rubric according to the total score.

Vocabulary Assessments

# Assessing Vocabulary in Context: Level I, Fiction
## Individual Record

Name _____ Grade _____ Date _____

### *The Best Cat*

Check ✓ one:　　Instructional Level: _____　　Independent Level: _____

| Vocabulary Word (✓ 5 Words Selected) | | Meaning | Student Response |
|---|---|---|---|
| | best, p. 2 | Better than any others | 0　1　2　3 |
| | furry, p. 2 | Having lots of fur, or soft hair, covering the body | 0　1　2　3 |
| | promise, p. 4 | To make a statement that you will do something or behave a certain way | 0　1　2　3 |
| | friendly, p. 6 | Nice; behaving in a way that is pleasant and kind | 0　1　2　3 |
| | everywhere, p. 6 | All around; in every place | 0　1　2　3 |
| | choose, p. 9 | To pick, to select something from a variety of choices | 0　1　2　3 |
| | many, p. 14 | A large number of | 0　1　2　3 |
| | soft, p. 15 | Quiet | 0　1　2　3 |
| | | **Total Score** | |

**Score:**

**0**　Did not respond or said "I don't know"

**1**　Made a response that is in some way related to the meaning of the word (any definition of that word)

**2**　Responded with a definition that is approximately the meaning of the word (same definition of the word as used in the text)

**3**　Responded with a full definition of the word (precise definition used in the text)

| Level | Unsatisfactory | Satisfactory | Excellent |
|---|---|---|---|
| A, B, C | 0–4 | 5–6 | 7–9 |
| D, E, F, G | 0–6 | 7–8 | 9–12 |
| H, I, J, K, L, M, N | 0–8 | 9–11 | 12–15 |

▶ Circle the rubric according to the total score.

Vocabulary Assessments

## Assessing Vocabulary in Context: Level I, Nonfiction
**Individual Record**

Name _____  Grade _____  Date _____

### *All About Koalas*

Check ✓ one:   Instructional Level: _____   Independent Level: _____

| Vocabulary Word (✓ 5 Words Selected) | | Meaning | Student Response |
|---|---|---|---|
| | claws, p. 3 | Sharp, thin, curved nails on animal's toes | 0  1  2  3 |
| | thick, p. 4 | Growing close together; dense | 0  1  2  3 |
| | fluffy, p. 5 | Having lots of soft hair | 0  1  2  3 |
| | leaves, p. 6 | Thin, flat, green parts that stick out from a plant's stem or shoots | 0  1  2  3 |
| | joey, p. 9 | A baby koala | 0  1  2  3 |
| | special, p. 10 | Different from the rest; not ordinary | 0  1  2  3 |
| | travels, p. 13 | Goes from one place to another | 0  1  2  3 |
| | thumbs, p. 13 | Short thick fingers set apart from the other fingers on the hand or paw | 0  1  2  3 |
| | | **Total Score** | |

**Score:**

**0**  Did not respond or said "I don't know"

**1**  Made a response that is in some way related to the meaning of the word (any definition of that word)

**2**  Responded with a definition that is approximately the meaning of the word (same definition of the word as used in the text)

**3**  Responded with a full definition of the word (precise definition used in the text)

| Level | Unsatisfactory | Satisfactory | Excellent |
|---|---|---|---|
| A, B, C | 0–4 | 5–6 | 7–9 |
| D, E, F, G | 0–6 | 7–8 | 9–12 |
| H, I, J, K, L, M, N | 0–8 | 9–11 | 12–15 |

▶ Circle the rubric according to the total score.

# Assessing Vocabulary in Context: Level J, Fiction
## Individual Record

Name _____  Grade _____  Date _____

### Our New Neighbors

Check ✓ one:   Instructional Level: _____   Independent Level: _____

| Vocabulary Word (✓ 5 Words Selected) | | Meaning | Student Response |
|---|---|---|---|
| | envelope, p. 2 | A piece of folded paper to put a letter in | 0  1  2  3 |
| | hope, p. 5 | To want or wish for something | 0  1  2  3 |
| | corner, p. 6 | The place were two sides meet | 0  1  2  3 |
| | neighbors, p. 7 | People who live nearby | 0  1  2  3 |
| | called, p. 7 | Spoke in a loud voice | 0  1  2  3 |
| | excited, p. 9 | Having strong feelings; thrilled | 0  1  2  3 |
| | mystery, p. 9 | Something that is not known or understood | 0  1  2  3 |
| | leaned, p. 14 | Tilted toward; rested against | 0  1  2  3 |
| | | **Total Score** | |

**Score:**

**0**   Did not respond or said "I don't know"

**1**   Made a response that is in some way related to the meaning of the word (any definition of that word)

**2**   Responded with a definition that is approximately the meaning of the word (same definition of the word as used in the text)

**3**   Responded with a full definition of the word (precise definition used in the text)

| Level | Unsatisfactory | Satisfactory | Excellent |
|---|---|---|---|
| A, B, C | 0–4 | 5–6 | 7–9 |
| D, E, F, G | 0–6 | 7–8 | 9–12 |
| H, I, J, K, L, M, N | 0–8 | 9–11 | 12–15 |

▶ Circle the rubric according to the total score.

Vocabulary Assessments

# Assessing Vocabulary in Context: Level J, Nonfiction
## Individual Record

Name _____ Grade _____ Date _____

### *More Than a Pet*

Check ✓ one:   Instructional Level: _____   Independent Level: _____

| Vocabulary Word (✓ 5 Words Selected) | | Meaning | Student Response |
|---|---|---|---|
| | therapy dogs, p. 3 | Dogs that help people feel better | 0 1 2 3 |
| | service dogs, p. 3 | Dogs that work | 0 1 2 3 |
| | hospital, p. 4 | A place where sick or injured people go to get care | 0 1 2 3 |
| | cheer, p. 7 | To make happier | 0 1 2 3 |
| | visits, p. 8 | Sees in order to comfort or help; spends time with | 0 1 2 3 |
| | gentle, p. 9 | Not harsh or rough; mild | 0 1 2 3 |
| | trained, p. 11 | Taught | 0 1 2 3 |
| | harness, p. 12 | Something with straps and fastenings that is placed on an animal | 0 1 2 3 |
| | | **Total Score** | |

**Score:**

**0**  Did not respond or said "I don't know"

**1**  Made a response that is in some way related to the meaning of the word (any definition of that word)

**2**  Responded with a definition that is approximately the meaning of the word (same definition of the word as used in the text)

**3**  Responded with a full definition of the word (precise definition used in the text)

| Level | Unsatisfactory | Satisfactory | Excellent |
|---|---|---|---|
| A, B, C | 0–4 | 5–6 | 7–9 |
| D, E, F, G | 0–6 | 7–8 | 9–12 |
| H, I, J, K, L, M, N | 0–8 | 9–11 | 12–15 |

▶ Circle the rubric according to the total score.

# Assessing Vocabulary in Context: Level K, Fiction
## Individual Record

Name _____ Grade _____ Date _____

### Edwin's Haircut

Check ✓ one:    Instructional Level: _____    Independent Level: _____

| Vocabulary Word (✓ 5 Words Selected) | | Meaning | Student Response |
|---|---|---|---|
| | shaggy, p. 2 | Having overly long hair | 0  1  2  3 |
| | complained, p. 6 | Found fault with | 0  1  2  3 |
| | crooked, p. 7 | Not straight | 0  1  2  3 |
| | agreed, p. 7 | Had the same opinion | 0  1  2  3 |
| | remembered, p. 9 | Thought of again | 0  1  2  3 |
| | sure, p. 11 | Certain; having no doubt | 0  1  2  3 |
| | appeared, p. 14 | Arrive; came | 0  1  2  3 |
| | barber, p. 16 | A person who cuts hair | 0  1  2  3 |
| | | **Total Score** | |

**Score:**

**0**  Did not respond or said "I don't know"

**1**  Made a response that is in some way related to the meaning of the word (any definition of that word)

**2**  Responded with a definition that is approximately the meaning of the word (same definition of the word as used in the text)

**3**  Responded with a full definition of the word (precise definition used in the text)

| Level | Unsatisfactory | Satisfactory | Excellent |
|---|---|---|---|
| A, B, C | 0–4 | 5–6 | 7–9 |
| D, E, F, G | 0–6 | 7–8 | 9–12 |
| H, I, J, K, L, M, N | 0–8 | 9–11 | 12–15 |

▶ Circle the rubric according to the total score.

Vocabulary Assessments

# Assessing Vocabulary in Context: Level K, Nonfiction
## Individual Record

Name _____ Grade _____ Date _____

## Surprising Animal Senses

Check ✓ one:    Instructional Level: _____    Independent Level: _____

| Vocabulary Word (✓ 5 Words Selected) | | Meaning | Student Response |
|---|---|---|---|
| | senses, p. 2 | The body's way of taking in stimuli; sight, smell, hearing, touch, and taste | 0  1  2  3 |
| | starfish, p. 5 | A sea animal with arms that extend from the center, to make a star shape | 0  1  2  3 |
| | rough, p. 6 | Having a surface that is uneven; not smooth | 0  1  2  3 |
| | sandpaper, p. 6 | Paper with rough material glued to it, intended to be rubbed on a surface to make the surface smooth | 0  1  2  3 |
| | whiskers, p. 7 | Long, thick hairs growing on an animal | 0  1  2  3 |
| | openings, p. 7 | Holes; open places; spaces to pass through | 0  1  2  3 |
| | whisper, p. 12 | To talk in a low, soft voice | 0  1  2  3 |
| | track, p. 15 | To follow the tracks of something or someone | 0  1  2  3 |
| | | **Total Score** | |

**Score:**

**0**  Did not respond or said "I don't know"

**1**  Made a response that is in some way related to the meaning of the word (any definition of that word)

**2**  Responded with a definition that is approximately the meaning of the word (same definition of the word as used in the text)

**3**  Responded with a full definition of the word (precise definition used in the text)

| Level | Unsatisfactory | Satisfactory | Excellent |
|---|---|---|---|
| A, B, C | 0–4 | 5–6 | 7–9 |
| D, E, F, G | 0–6 | 7–8 | 9–12 |
| H, I, J, K, L, M, N | 0–8 | 9–11 | 12–15 |

▶ Circle the rubric according to the total score.

# Assessing Vocabulary in Context: Level L, Fiction
## Individual Record

Name _____   Grade _____   Date _____

## *Dog Stories*

Check ✓ one:   Instructional Level: _____   Independent Level: _____

| Vocabulary Word (✓ 5 Words Selected) | | Meaning | Student Response |
|---|---|---|---|
| | author, p. 5 | A person who writes a book or story | 0 1 2 3 |
| | wonderful, p. 7 | Great; very special | 0 1 2 3 |
| | hero, p. 7 | The most important character in a story | 0 1 2 3 |
| | photograph, p. 8 | A picture taken by a camera | 0 1 2 3 |
| | warned, p. 8 | To let know ahead of time | 0 1 2 3 |
| | leash, p. 10 | A strap or chain that is used to keep a dog close by | 0 1 2 3 |
| | dove, p. 10 | Jumped into; plunged | 0 1 2 3 |
| | dangling, p. 10 | Hanging | 0 1 2 3 |
| | addressed, p. 14 | Directed to; having someone's address | 0 1 2 3 |
| | disappointed, p. 15 | Let down | 0 1 2 3 |
| | | **Total Score** | |

**Score:**

**0**   Did not respond or said "I don't know"

**1**   Made a response that is in some way related to the meaning of the word (any definition of that word)

**2**   Responded with a definition that is approximately the meaning of the word (same definition of the word as used in the text)

**3**   Responded with a full definition of the word (precise definition used in the text)

| Level | Unsatisfactory | Satisfactory | Excellent |
|---|---|---|---|
| A, B, C | 0–4 | 5–6 | 7–9 |
| D, E, F, G | 0–6 | 7–8 | 9–12 |
| H, I, J, K, L, M, N | 0–8 | 9–11 | 12–15 |

▶ Circle the rubric according to the total score.

Vocabulary Assessments

# Assessing Vocabulary in Context: Level L, Nonfiction
## Individual Record

Name _____  Grade _____  Date _____

## Giants of the Sea

Check ✓ one:   Instructional Level: _____   Independent Level: _____

| Vocabulary Word (✓ 5 Words Selected) | | Meaning | Student Response |
|---|---|---|---|
| | underwater, p. 6 | Below the surface of the water | 0 1 2 3 |
| | lungs, p. 7 | A organ in the chest that is used for breathing | 0 1 2 3 |
| | blowholes, p. 7 | Hole found on the top of whales' heads, used for breathing | 0 1 2 3 |
| | spray, p. 8 | A mist of tiny drops | 0 1 2 3 |
| | dive, p. 9 | To plunge headfirst into water | 0 1 2 3 |
| | surface, p. 10 | The outside or top of something | 0 1 2 3 |
| | communicate, p. 12 | To exchange information | 0 1 2 3 |
| | whistle, p. 12 | To make a high-pitched sound by blowing | 0 1 2 3 |
| | bounce, p. 13 | To hit against a surface and come back | 0 1 2 3 |
| | orca, p. 15 | Killer whale | 0 1 2 3 |
| | | **Total Score** | |

**Score:**

**0**  Did not respond or said "I don't know"

**1**  Made a response that is in some way related to the meaning of the word (any definition of that word)

**2**  Responded with a definition that is approximately the meaning of the word (same definition of the word as used in the text)

**3**  Responded with a full definition of the word (precise definition used in the text)

| Level | Unsatisfactory | Satisfactory | Excellent |
|---|---|---|---|
| A, B, C | 0–4 | 5–6 | 7–9 |
| D, E, F, G | 0–6 | 7–8 | 9–12 |
| H, I, J, K, L, M, N | 0–8 | 9–11 | 12–15 |

▶ Circle the rubric according to the total score.

# Assessing Vocabulary in Context: Level M, Fiction
## Individual Record

Name _____   Grade _____   Date _____

### The Thing About Nathan

Check ✓ one:   Instructional Level: _____   Independent Level: _____

| Vocabulary Word (✓ 5 Words Selected) | | Meaning | Student Response |
|---|---|---|---|
| | herd, p. 2 | A group of the same kind of animals all living together | 0 1 2 3 |
| | neat, p. 3 | Tidy; clean; orderly | 0 1 2 3 |
| | trade, p. 4 | Swap; exchange one thing for another | 0 1 2 3 |
| | supposed, p. 4 | To have to do something; to be required | 0 1 2 3 |
| | bursting, p. 6 | Filled to the breaking point | 0 1 2 3 |
| | kits, p. 6 | Sets of parts or pieces that are to be put together | 0 1 2 3 |
| | declared, p. 7 | Said in a formal way | 0 1 2 3 |
| | tossing, p. 12 | Throwing lightly | 0 1 2 3 |
| | seriously, p. 13 | To a great degree; extremely | 0 1 2 3 |
| | described, p. 15 | Told in detail | 0 1 2 3 |
| | | **Total Score** | |

**Score:**

**0**  Did not respond or said "I don't know"

**1**  Made a response that is in some way related to the meaning of the word (any definition of that word)

**2**  Responded with a definition that is approximately the meaning of the word (same definition of the word as used in the text)

**3**  Responded with a full definition of the word (precise definition used in the text)

| Level | Unsatisfactory | Satisfactory | Excellent |
|---|---|---|---|
| A, B, C | 0–4 | 5–6 | 7–9 |
| D, E, F, G | 0–6 | 7–8 | 9–12 |
| H, I, J, K, L, M, N | 0–8 | 9–11 | 12–15 |

▶ Circle the rubric according to the total score.

# Assessing Vocabulary in Context: Level M, Nonfiction
## Individual Record

Name _____  Grade _____  Date _____

### *The Life of a Monarch Butterfly*

Check ✓ one:  Instructional Level: _____  Independent Level: _____

| Vocabulary Word (✓ 5 Words Selected) | | Meaning | Student Response |
|---|---|---|---|
| | speck, p. 2 | A small spot | 0  1  2  3 |
| | tiny, p. 2 | Very small | 0  1  2  3 |
| | female, p. 3 | Being the gender that gives birth | 0  1  2  3 |
| | hatch, p. 4 | To come out of the egg | 0  1  2  3 |
| | expecting, p. 4 | Thinking something will happen | 0  1  2  3 |
| | tight, p. 5 | Fitting too closely | 0  1  2  3 |
| | underneath, p. 6 | Directly below or under | 0  1  2  3 |
| | chrysalis, p. 8 | The covering that protects a young moth or butterfly | 0  1  2  3 |
| | clings, p. 12 | Holds on tightly to something | 0  1  2  3 |
| | flutter, p. 15 | To move the wings quickly | 0  1  2  3 |
| | | **Total Score** | |

**Score:**

**0** Did not respond or said "I don't know"

**1** Made a response that is in some way related to the meaning of the word (any definition of that word)

**2** Responded with a definition that is approximately the meaning of the word (same definition of the word as used in the text)

**3** Responded with a full definition of the word (precise definition used in the text)

| Level | Unsatisfactory | Satisfactory | Excellent |
|---|---|---|---|
| A, B, C | 0–4 | 5–6 | 7–9 |
| D, E, F, G | 0–6 | 7–8 | 9–12 |
| H, I, J, K, L, M, N | 0–8 | 9–11 | 12–15 |

▶ Circle the rubric according to the total score.

# Assessing Vocabulary in Context: Level N, Fiction
## Individual Record

Name _____ Grade _____ Date _____

### *The Big Snow*

Check ✓ one:    Instructional Level: _____    Independent Level: _____

| Vocabulary Word (✓ 5 Words Selected) | | Meaning | Student Response |
|---|---|---|---|
| | finally, p. 2 | Happening at the end of a period of time | 0  1  2  3 |
| | ankle-deep, p. 2 | Having a depth just above the top of the feet | 0  1  2  3 |
| | apartment, p. 3 | A room or rooms used as a home | 0  1  2  3 |
| | pretend, p. 3 | To make believe | 0  1  2  3 |
| | vanished, p. 4 | Disappeared, or passed from sight | 0  1  2  3 |
| | ignore, p. 6 | To not pay attention to | 0  1  2  3 |
| | uneasy, p. 6 | Not comfortable; worried | 0  1  2  3 |
| | nervous, p. 8 | Fearful; worried | 0  1  2  3 |
| | elevator, p. 11 | A small room used to carry people or things up and down from one floor of a building to another | 0  1  2  3 |
| | exhausted, p. 15 | Tired; out of energy | 0  1  2  3 |
| | | **Total Score** | |

**Score:**

**0**  Did not respond or said "I don't know"

**1**  Made a response that is in some way related to the meaning of the word (any definition of that word)

**2**  Responded with a definition that is approximately the meaning of the word (same definition of the word as used in the text)

**3**  Responded with a full definition of the word (precise definition used in the text)

| Level | Unsatisfactory | Satisfactory | Excellent |
|---|---|---|---|
| A, B, C | 0–4 | 5–6 | 7–9 |
| D, E, F, G | 0–6 | 7–8 | 9–12 |
| H, I, J, K, L, M, N | 0–8 | 9–11 | 12–15 |

▶ Circle the rubric according to the total score.

Vocabulary Assessments

# Assessing Vocabulary in Context: Level N, Nonfiction
## Individual Record

Name _____ Grade _____ Date _____

## *Exploring Caves*

Check ✓ one:  Instructional Level: _____  Independent Level: _____

| Vocabulary Word (✓ 5 Words Selected) | | Meaning | Student Response |
|---|---|---|---|
| | caverns, p. 2 | Large caves | 0  1  2  3 |
| | invisible, p. 4 | Not able to be seen | 0  1  2  3 |
| | seeps, p. 4 | Moves slowly through small cracks or spaces | 0  1  2  3 |
| | continues, p. 5 | Carries on; keeps going | 0  1  2  3 |
| | sites, p. 6 | Places where a particular thing is located or can be found | 0  1  2  3 |
| | experts, p. 6 | People who know a lot about a subject or have a special skill | 0  1  2  3 |
| | prepared, p. 7 | To be ready for something | 0  1  2  3 |
| | sturdy, p. 7 | Strong and well made or built | 0  1  2  3 |
| | entrances, p. 11 | Ways in to something | 0  1  2  3 |
| | columns, p. 14 | Tall, vertical, round posts | 0  1  2  3 |
| | | Total Score | |

**Score:**

**0**  Did not respond or said "I don't know"

**1**  Made a response that is in some way related to the meaning of the word (any definition of that word)

**2**  Responded with a definition that is approximately the meaning of the word (same definition of the word as used in the text)

**3**  Responded with a full definition of the word (precise definition used in the text)

| Level | Unsatisfactory | Satisfactory | Excellent |
|---|---|---|---|
| A, B, C | 0–4 | 5–6 | 7–9 |
| D, E, F, G | 0–6 | 7–8 | 9–12 |
| H, I, J, K, L, M, N | 0–8 | 9–11 | 12–15 |

▶ Circle the rubric according to the total score.

# Resources

In this section, you will find a variety of helpful forms and tools that are referenced in the *Benchmark Assessment Guide*. You can photocopy the pages from this book or print them from the *Forms CD-ROM*.

# Assessment at-a-Glance

**Preparation**    **Materials**

▶ Benchmark Books

▶ Recording Forms

▶ Student Writing Materials

▶ F and P Calculator

▶ Assessment Summary Form

**Administration**

1. **Record** student information on the Recording Form.

2. Enter number of words (**RW**) in the text on the calculator.

3. Read the **title** and the **introduction** to the child.

4. Start the **timer** on the calculator.

5. Have the student start **reading orally.**

6. **Code** the reading behavior on the form.

7. Stop the **timer** on the calculator and record the time on the form.

8. Enter number of **errors** and **self-corrections** on the calculator.

9. Make brief notes about **fluency** and/or circle a fluency rating (levels C–N).

10. Have a **conversation** with the student about the text. Check off items the child talks about. Use prompts as needed to probe for understanding. Score each area and decide on the additional point immediately after the conversation.

11. Read the **writing prompt** to the child (if needed). Have the child begin writing (about 20 minutes maximum).

12. Press buttons (**Accur. %, SC, WPM**) to obtain and record scores.

13. Repeat the process until you **determine** the independent, instructional, and hard text level.

14. **Record** the results on the Assessment Summary Form.

Resources

# Coding and Scoring Errors at-a-Glance

| Behavior | What the Reader Does | How to Code | Example | How to Score | |
|---|---|---|---|---|---|
| Accurate Reading | Reads words correctly | Do not mark or place check (✓) above word. | no mark or $\dfrac{✓}{\text{Kate}}$ | | No error |
| Substitution | Gives an incorrect response. | Write the substituted word above the word. | $\dfrac{\text{her}}{\text{Kate's}}$ | Substitution, not corrected | 1 error |
| | | | | Substitution, self-corrected (SC) | No error; 1 SC |
| Multiple Substitutions | Makes several attempts at a word | Write each of the substitutions in sequence above the word. | $\dfrac{\text{little\|some\|him}}{\text{his}}$ | Multiple substitutions, not corrected | 1 error for each incorrect word in text |
| | | | $\dfrac{\text{touch\|teeth\|SC}}{\text{tooth}}$ | Multiple substitutions, self-corrected (SC) | No error; 1 SC |
| | | | $\dfrac{\text{to\|touch\|teeth}}{\text{tooth}}$ | Multiple misreadings of the same word not corrected | 1 error for each word in text |
| | | | $\dfrac{\text{Kathy\|Kelly}}{\text{Kate}}$ | Multiple misreadings of names and proper nouns | 1 error first time missed; no errors after that |
| | | | $\dfrac{\text{It's}}{\text{It is}}\ \dfrac{\text{Do not}}{\text{Don't}}$ | Misreading contractions (reads contraction as two words or two words as contraction) | 1 error each time |
| Self-correction | Corrects a previous error | Write the error over the word, followed by SC. | $\dfrac{\text{teeth\|SC}}{\text{tooth}}$ | | No error; 1 SC |
| Insertion | Adds a word that is not in the text | Write in the inserted word using a carat (^). | loose ∧ | | 1 error per word inserted |
| Omission | Gives no response to a word | Place a dash (–) above the word. | $\dfrac{-}{\text{Very}}$ | Skipping a word | 1 error per word |
| | | | | Skipping a line | 1 error per word |
| Repetition | Reads the same word again | Write R above the word. | R | | No error |

*Coding system developed by Marie Clay as part of the running record system in* An Observation Survey of Early Literacy Achievement, Revised Second Edition, *2006, Heinemann.*

# Coding and Scoring Errors at-a-Glance (continued)

| Behavior | What the Reader Does | How to Code | Example | How to Score | |
|----------|---------------------|-------------|---------|--------------|--|
| Repeated Repetitions | Reads the same word more than once | Write R above the word for the first repetition and then write a number for the additional repetitions. | $R_2$ $R_3$ | | No error |
| Rereading | Returns to the beginning of sentence or phrase to read again | Write R with an arrow back to the place where rereading began. | R | | No error |
| | Rereads and self-corrects | Write R with an arrow back to the place where rereading began and SC at point of self-correction | tooth to come\|SC $^R$<br>tooth to   fall | | No error; 1 SC |
| Appeal | Verbally asks for help | Write A above the word. | $\dfrac{A}{very}$ | Follow up with "You try it." | No error |
| "You Try It" | The child appeals, the teacher responds with "You try it." | Write Y after the word. | $\dfrac{A}{very}$ \| Y | "You try it" followed by correct word | No error |
| | | | | "You try it" followed by omission, incorrect word, or Told | 1 error |
| Told | Child doesn't attempt word even after "You try it." | Write T after the word or the Y. | $\dfrac{A}{very}$\|Y\|T   $\dfrac{A}{very}$\|T | | 1 error |
| Spelling Aloud | The child spells the word by saying the names of letters. | Write the letters in all capital letters. | $\dfrac{B\text{-}U\text{-}T}{But}$ | Spelling followed by correct word | No error |
| | | | | Spelling followed by incorrect word | 1 error |
| Sounding Out | The child makes the sounds associated with the letters in the word. | Write the letters in lowercase with hyphens between them. | $\dfrac{n\text{-}o\text{-}t}{not}$ | "Sounding out" followed by correct word | No error; no SC |
| | | | $\dfrac{l\text{-}o\text{-}s}{loose}$ \|lose | "Sounding out" followed by incorrect word | 1 error |
| | | | $\dfrac{f\text{-}}{come}$ \| SC | Sounding the first letter incorrectly and then saying the word correctly | No error; 1 SC |

*Coding system developed by Marie Clay as part of the running record system in* An Observation Survey of Early Literacy Achievement, Revised Second Edition, *2006, Heinemann.*

Name: _____ Date: _____

| Guide for Observing and Noting Reading Behaviors | Notes |
|---|---|
| **1. Attention to Print Features**<br>*Does the reader:*<br>• Move left to right across a line of print?<br>• Return to the left for a new line?<br>• Match word by word while reading a line or more of print?<br>• Recognize a few easy high frequency words? | |
| **2. Detecting Errors**<br>*Does the reader:*<br>• Hesitate at an unknown word?<br>• Stop at an unknown word?<br>• Stop at an unknown word and appeal for help?<br>• Stop after an error?<br>• Notice mismatches?<br>• Notice when an attempt does not look right?<br>• Notice when an attempt does not sound right?<br>• Notice when an attempt does not make sense?<br>• Reread to confirm reading?<br>• Use knowledge of some high frequency words to check on reading?<br>• Check one source of information with another?<br>• Check an attempt that makes sense with language?<br>• Check an attempt that makes sense with the letters (visual information)?<br>• Use language structure to check on reading?<br>• Request help after making several attempts? | |
| **3. Self-Correcting**<br>*Does the reader:*<br>• Reread and try again until accurate?<br>• Stop after an error and make another attempt?<br>• Stop after an error and make multiple attempts until accurate?<br>• Reread to self-correct?<br>• Work actively to solve mismatches?<br>• Self-correct errors some of the time?<br>• Self-correct errors most of the time? | |
| **4. Searching for and Using Information**<br>**Meaning**<br>*Does the reader:*<br>• Make meaningful attempts at unknown words?<br>• Use the meaning of the story or text to predict unknown words?<br>• Reread to gather more information to solve a word?<br>• Reread and use the meaning of the sentence?<br>• Reread to search for more details—information, characters, plot?<br>• Reread to gather information to clarify confusions?<br>• Use headings and titles to think about the meaning of a section of text?<br>• Use information in the pictures to help in understanding a text?<br>• Use knowledge of the genre (and its characteristics) to help in understanding a text?<br>• Use knowledge of the genre (and its characteristics) to help in finding information?<br>• Use readers' tools to help in finding information (glossary, index)?<br><br>**Structure**<br>*Does the reader:*<br>• Use knowledge of oral language to solve unknown words?<br>• Reread to see if a word "sounds right" in a sentence?<br>• Reread to correct using language structure? | |

| Guide for Observing . . . (cont.) | Notes |
|---|---|
| **Visual Information**<br>*Does the reader:*<br>• Use the visual information to solve words?<br>• Use the sound of the first letter(s) to attempt or solve a word?<br>• Use some, most, or all of the visual information to solve words?<br>• Use sound analysis to solve a word?<br>• Make attempts that are visually similar?<br>• Use knowledge of a high frequency word to problem solve?<br>• Search for more visual information within a word to solve it?<br>• Use analogy to solve unknown words?<br>• Use syllables to solve words?<br>• Use prefixes and suffixes to take apart and recognize words?<br>• Use inflectional endings to problem solve words?<br>• Recognize most words quickly and easily?<br>• Reread and use the sound of the first letter to solve a word?<br>• Problem solve unknown words quickly and efficiently?<br>• Work actively to solve words?<br>• Use two or three sources of information together in attempts at words?<br>• Use all sources of information flexibly to solve words?<br>• Use all sources of information in an orchestrated way? | |
| **5. Solving Words**<br>*Does the reader:*<br>• Recognize a core of high frequency words quickly?<br>• Recognize most words quickly and easily?<br>• Use a variety of flexible ways to take words apart?<br>• Use the meaning of the sentences to solve words?<br>• Use the structure of the sentence to solve words?<br>• Use some of the visual information to solve words?<br>• Use known word parts to solve words?<br>• Use sound analysis (sounding out)?<br>• Use analogy to solve words?<br>• Make attempts that are visually similar?<br>• Use the sound of the first letter to solve words?<br>• Work actively to solve words?<br>• Use known words or parts to solve unknown words?<br>• Use syllables to problem solve?<br>• Use prefixes and suffixes to take words apart?<br>• Use inflectional endings to take words apart?<br>• Use sentence context to derive the meaning of words?<br>• Use base words and root words to derive the meaning of words?<br>• Make connections among words to understand their meaning? | |
| **6. Maintaining Fluency**<br>*Does the reader:*<br>• Read without pointing?<br>• Read word groups (phrases)?<br>• Put words together?<br>• Read smoothly?<br>• Read the punctuation?<br>• Make the voice go down at periods?<br>• Make the voice go up at question marks?<br>• Pause briefly at commas, dashes, and hyphens?<br>• Read dialogue with intonation or expression?<br>• Stress the appropriate words to convey accurate meaning?<br>• Read at a good rate—not too fast and not too slow? | |
| **7. Other** | |

Resources

# Scoring and Analysis at-a-Glance

**Score Part I Oral Reading on the Recording Form scoring page**

1. **Accuracy Rate** Circle the number of errors on the graph to determine the percent of words read correctly.

2. **Self-Correction Ratio** Number of errors + Number of self-corrections [÷] = 1: ___

3. **Fluency Score** Circle a score.

4. **Reading Rate** Record or calculate the words per minute (WPM) read. Number of timed seconds read [÷] Number of running words [×] 60 = WPM

**Score Part II Comprehension Conversation with the key understandings chart on the Recording Form**
5. **Comprehension Conversation**

   a. Assign points in each category (Within, Beyond, About the text)

   b. Total the category scores, adding a point if appropriate for additional understandings, and circle the final evaluation in the Guide to Total Score box.

**Score Part III Writing About Reading (optional) on the Recording Form**

6. Circle the appropriate score on the scoring key.

**Complete the Assessment Summary.**

7. Record data from the Recording Form on the Assessment Summary form.

8. Determine two Benchmark Levels and write them in the box in the upper right corner of the Assessment Summary.

**Benchmark Independent Level**
**Levels A–K:** 95–100% accuracy with excellent or satisfactory comprehension
**Levels L–Z:** 98–100% accuracy with excellent or satisfactory comprehension

**Benchmark Instructional Level**
**Levels A–K:** 90–94% accuracy with excellent or satisfactory comprehension or 95–100% accuracy with limited comprehension
**Levels L–Z:** 95–97% accuracy with excellent or satisfactory comprehension or 98–100% accuracy with limited comprehension

9. Review accuracy, use of sources of information, problem solving, self-correction ratio, fluency, and comprehension to determine **Recommended Placement Level.**

10. Use the Guide for Observing and Noting Reading Behaviors (in the *Assessment Guide* and *Assessment Forms* book and CD-ROM) to make additional comments and make notes about instructional implications at the bottom of the Assessment Summary form.

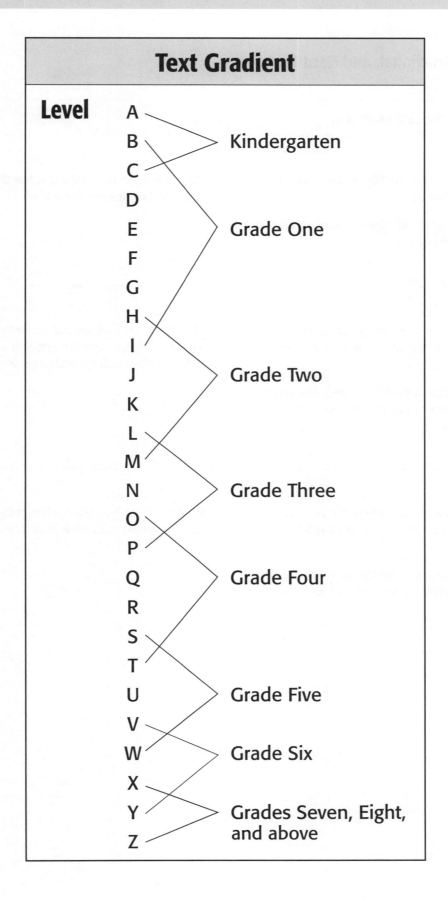

# Text Gradient

**Level**

A
B — Kindergarten
C
D
E — Grade One
F
G
H
I — Grade Two
J
K
L
M — Grade Three
N
O
P — Grade Four
Q
R
S
T — Grade Five
U
V
W — Grade Six
X
Y — Grades Seven, Eight, and above
Z

# Finding Easy, Instructional, and Hard Texts

| If the first book is... | Then... |
|---|---|
| **Easy**<br><br>**Levels A–K:** Student reads at 95–100% accuracy with excellent or satisfactory comprehension.<br><br>**Levels L–Z:** Student reads at 98–100% accuracy with excellent or satisfactory comprehension. | Move to a higher level text and repeat the same process until the student reads a text that is hard. |
| **Instructional**<br><br>**Levels A–K**: Student reads at 90–94% accuracy with excellent or satisfactory comprehension <u>or</u> 95–100% accuracy with limited comprehension.<br><br>**Levels L–Z**: Student reads at 95–97% accuracy with excellent or satisfactory comprehension <u>or</u> 98–100% accuracy with limited comprehension. | Move to a lower level text and repeat the same process until the student reads a text that is easy and move to a higher level text until the student reads a text that is hard. |
| **Hard**<br><br>**Levels A–K**: Student reads at below 90% accuracy with any score on comprehension <u>or</u> 90–94% accuracy with limited comprehension.<br><br>**Levels L–Z**: Student reads at below 95% accuracy with any score on comprehension <u>or</u> 95–97% accuracy with limited comprehension. | Move to a lower level text and repeat the same process until the student reads a text at an instructional level. |